D

- by Ro

Wakan Tanka Publishers

Dog Language
- by Roger Abrantes

Special revised and updated English version

Wakan Tanka Publishers

Published by Wakan Tanka Publishers.

Distributed by:
  Dogwise Publishing
  403 South Mission Street
  Wenatchee, WA 98801
  509-663-9115   www.dogwisepublishing.com

ISBN: 978-0-9660484-0-7

Typeset in Times 11 pt at Lupus Forlag. Printed and bound in the USA.

Contents

'The only justification for our concepts and systems of concepts is that they serve to represent the complex of our experiences; beyond this they have no legitimacy'—Albert Einstein.

Foreword

This book has only been possible thanks to the work of many scientists to whom I wish to pay tribute; I will kindly ask readers to study the bibliography at the end. Their efforts and the research conducted since 1984 at the Etologisk Institute, Høng, Denmark, under my supervision, support the topics presented below.

Dog Language is an updated, highly revised and enlarged version of the original *'Hundesprog'* published in Danish in 1986. There have not been many new discoveries in canine behaviour since, but advances in the diagnosis and treatment of behaviour problems in dogs have compelled me to treat some entries with particular care.

Behaviour means *the way of acting*. Behaviour *is 'the actions or reactions of persons or things under given circumstances.'* [1] Behaviour means *'conduct, actions bearing, comportment'*. Everything in the way you or I, or our dogs, appear to one another is behaviour. The ultimate purpose of all behaviour is to cope with the necessities of life. Behaviour has no existence *per se*, no purpose in itself — it serves other goals. It is therefore frequently difficult to uncover the reasons and motives for behaviour. We can only understand specific displays by comparing the unknown traits of one species with the known patterns of another. This comparative method is often a rewarding and significant tool for the study of behaviour. Comparison means discovering not only similarities, but also differences. The former are useful in supporting new ideas and subsequent studies, but the latter are also fruitful, often answering the original question and raising new quests at the same time.

To observe objectively, without a single preconception, is impossible and remains nothing but a theoretical issue, a testimony of our incapacity to comply with our own standards. Problems arise with the very first question: to observe, yes, but what? The choice of what to observe is a restriction, the first breach to be crossed in order to comply with the rule of objectivity. Any journey of discovery needs a preconceived map, and mine is no exception.

Throughout this book I have pictured behaviour using the model that I describe in the first chapter *'The Evolution of Social Behaviour in Canids.'* It is only through an understanding of perspectives that we can appreciate individual contributions. A book about dog behaviour and communication without a broader survey of behaviour is not fair to the dog at all. On the contrary, it may give the reader a biased idea of what dog behaviour really is.

Of all the scientists whose work has contributed to this book, I believe the classic ethologists, and particularly Konrad Lorenz, influenced me most. John Maynard Smith and Richard Dawkins's theoretical issues, together with the field work of David Mech and Erik Zimen have also affected my thoughts. However, they bear no responsibility for my application of their theories, or for any errors I may have committed.

I thank Ian Dunbar for his faith in my book, his encouragement and his contribution to the understanding of companion animal behaviour.

I am indebted to my English editor Sarah Whitehead, a skilled pet behaviour counsellor herself, for her editorial work and for the suggestions she made. Thanks also to the staff of the Etologisk Institute and to Dr Birkes Poulsen for her valuable contributions; to Sandy Myers for all her support; to Alice Rasmussen for her marvellous drawings and co-operation and to Betina Riel Pedersen for the many hours she dedicated to the lay-out of this book.

Solbjerg, December 1996

Roger Abrantes

The Evolution Of Canine Social Behaviour*

The strategy of life

There is only one objective in life: to live long enough to pass half of one's genes to the next generation. This is the ultimate and universal goal for all living beings on this planet and there are as many strategies for achieving this objective as there are living forms.

Life is the activity of all organisms, from primitive forms such as blue-green algae, to complex ones like mammals. This activity falls into two major categories: metabolism and reproduction.

Metabolism is the physical and chemical process by which the organism uses energy from its environment for self-preservation. The energy source can be heat, from the sun, for example, or the chemical energy of ingested food. A living organism converts energy.

Molecules called *nucleic acids* control reproduction. *Deoxyribonucleic acid* (DNA) molecules can make copies of themselves. Reproduction involves making copies of the cell and results in copies of the organism itself, except in the case of viruses, which have a completely different strategy.

Life probably originated very early in the history of the earth when a sort of *replicator* somehow occurred. External sources of energy powered this primordial replicator that could make copies of itself. The first replicators eventually evolved into cells. Natural selection favoured the replicating molecules that could find energy most promptly, and evolution took care of the rest: procaryotes, nucleated cells, multicellular organisms, plants and animals. Evolutionary success depends on the ability of an organism to preserve its genes.

It is difficult to give a precise and general definition of life. However, in a

This chapter is a summary of the book of the same name. For the text in its entirety, including illustrations, please see 'The Evolution Of Canine Social Behaviour' by Roger Abrantes (Wakan Tanka, Illinois, 1997).

crude sense, we can say that an organism is alive if its *metabolism* and *reproduction* are operative. Everything threatening one or more of these functions is threatening to life.

There is never a single rewarding strategy for the organisms that exist in any given environment. The wild canids of the Serengeti offer a good example. Hunting dogs, *Lycaon pictus*, follow the herds of gnus, to feed the pack and their youngsters. The jackals, *Canis aureus*, on the other hand, stay in the same territory. The jackal hunts alone to sustain itself and its small family. They survive the drought by consuming any edible thing they can find.

These canids have found two different, but equally successful strategies in the same environment. Hunting dogs selected the strategy of staying together in large packs, persecuting prey and hunting it down. This has dramatically affected the spectrum of behaviour shown by the species, resulting in a large range of communication patterns.

Jackals, on the other hand, live in well-defined groups with few conflicts, because there are only two adults—one of each sex—plus one yearling and three or four pups. They do not need more than a limited repertoire of signals.

Nothing in life is free and nothing is free of consequences. Life is an exchange of one sort of energy for another. Hunting dog and jackal interact with their environment, and their behaviour, social or not, is invariably the best available strategy in the given circumstances.

There is, however, an alternative strategy. Widespread in the grasslands of Europe we find the continent's most common canine hunter, the fox, *Vulpes vulpes*. Also known as the red fox, it chose the strategy of loneliness. Foxes do not have complex communication patterns—they simply do not need them. To communicate presupposes a receiver, and the fox wanders alone. The behaviour of the fox reflects its strategy of life, as does the behaviour of the hunting dog and the jackal.

Strategies for living are many and varied. The *'preservation of favoured races in the struggle for life'*[2] happens according to numerous plans. In the family of canids alone, we find three distinct strategies:

1 - Solitary predators.
2 - Family pack hunters.
3 - Large pack hunters.

Communication patterns increase from 1 to 3. Being social has a price. Foxes resolve encounters with conspecifics using displays ruled by aggression or fear: attack, defence and flight.

Jackals are a bit different. The same mechanisms seen in the fox rule most encounters, but sometimes their behaviour assumes radically different measures—as for instance when a yearling female in the pack begins courting a strange male. The parents clearly show their disapproval, yet the yearling neither attacks them nor flees. The jackal shows a compromise behaviour we have become accustomed to call submission.

It is by observing the large pack hunters, like the wolf and our dog, Canis lupus familiaris, that we realise there is more to communication than aggression and fear.

What makes a social animal special is its ability to compromise, to win and lose and still get the best out of every situation.

Fear and anger, the fight for survival, the ability to find food or sexual partners, alliances with other species and so forth, are traits we find in many different animals of many different species. Some of them need conspecifics to survive and selection has favoured those among them who are best at co-operating. Time turned them into true champions in the art of compromise. Their secret is that they seldom exercise fear and aggression in social contexts. Instead, they have discovered other mechanisms with which to deal with conspecifics.

The social individual's original task was: 'to fulfil my will, without killing or harming the other, who I need for my survival and that of my offspring.' Evolution treated this like any other task, and time contributed to perfect the amazing ability of social self-awareness. The result was obvious. The individual developed two states of social self-awareness: self-confidence and its opposite, insecurity.

The social organism is thus an expert in solving social puzzles. It masters the application of fear and aggression, as well as behaviour motivated by what we shall now call social awareness.

Among these champions of compromise we find wolves, geese, chimpanzees, humans, and their best friends, dogs.

Motivation

In the past there have been two opposing theories as to what behaviour is: either animals learn everything, or they know what to do instinctively. In more recent times, scientists have built models explaining behaviour by combining elements of both. My own suggestion, which I use to define all concepts in the dictionary part of this book, falls into this category.

The most predominant school in explaining behaviour has been Behaviorism (J. B. Watson and B. F. Skinner).[3] Strict behaviourists assume that all behaviour is learned and formed through conditioning. To an orthodox behaviourist, animals must learn all behavioural patterns by means of trial and error. Extreme behaviourists also apply this rule to human behaviour.

There is, however, a completely different way to account for behaviour. Ethology assumes that much of what animals do is innate and performed instinctively. The genes programme entire behavioural sequences. Extreme ethologists maintain that all new behaviour results from maturation or imprinting.

The Nobel Prize-winning founders of Ethology, Konrad Lorenz, Nikolaas Tinbergen and Karl von Frisch[4], uncovered four strategies by which the genes programme behaviour: sign-stimuli or releasers, motor programmes, motivation or drives and learning, including imprinting.

Sign stimuli or *releasers* are signals that enable an animal to recognise a vital item, or another living creature, when it discovers them for the first time. We can easily detect sign-stimuli in communication, hunting and fear-elicited behaviour.

Motor programmes account for the display of another type of behaviour. The first motor programme studied was in the greylag goose; the egg-rolling response. When a goose sees an egg outside its nest, it stretches its neck until its bill reaches it, then gently rolls the egg back into the nest. Such a behaviour is a fixed-action pattern and ethologists maintain that it is innate.

An *instinct* is innate programming to perform a complex behavioural sequence without prior learning. Instinctive behaviour patterns are usually responses to specific stimuli such as feeding, mating, parenting and aggression. In each species instinctive behaviour develops according to natural selection. Instinctive behaviour helps an animal save energy in its ecological niche.

There is, however, another class of motor programme beside instincts. These are the learned patterns, like walking and swimming, that animals perform unconsciously after a time.

A central idea to understanding behaviour is *motivation. Motivation* is what compels an animal to do what it does.

We must thus define *motivation* exclusively with the law of causality: *every effect has a cause*. What are the causes? At first, we may answer by saying that animals are motivated by *drives*: self-preservation motivates hunting, sex motivates mating and aggression motivates the expulsion of a rival.

However, drives operate through an intricate system comprising of many behaviour patterns, some of which are inborn, while others develop through interactions with the environment. In the end, we face a new problem: what is a *drive*?

A *drive* is a force, an urge onward, a basic need, a compulsive energy.

Some psychologists have been keen to stress that motivation aims at reducing stimulation to its lowest possible level. Thus, an organism seeks the behaviour most likely to mean *no stimulation*. Recent theories of motivation, however, view humans as seeking to *optimise*, rather than minimise, stimulation. This accounts for exploratory behaviour, variety-seeking behaviour and curiosity.

Behaviour can also be explained in evolutionary terms, as Maynard Smith and Richard Dawkins have done. [5]

However, we must remember that scientific models are just our way of trying to understand the environment and our place in it. *'Reality is independent... of what you or I, or any finite number of men may think about it,'* in the words of Charles Sanders Peirce [6].

The concept of motivation is highly relevant to communication patterns. There is no behaviour without motivation. Most of the dog's facial expressions and body postures are motivated by fear, aggression, dominance/superiority and/or submission/inferiority. Motivation is also vital when teaching a dog various tricks or exercises.

Fear

Fear [7]
1. Fear is a feeling of agitation and anxiety caused by the presence or imminence of danger.
2. A state marked by this feeling.
3. Reverence or awe, as towards a deity.
4. A reason for dread or apprehension.

Fear is generally regarded as an unpleasant emotion; the expectation or the awareness of danger or pain causes fear. It is also agitation or dismay in the anticipation or presence of danger. The two definitions are the same, only the first defines it from a psychological perspective and the second from a behavioural point of view. The interesting point is that we use the word fear interchangeably with both meanings, yet we know little or nothing about the inner states of animals' minds.

The third definition is also interesting. It implies that fear may be something other than a behaviour elicited by danger. It also suggests that we may mistakenly call *reverence* fear, which is an attractive explanation of certain behaviour patterns in social animals.

What we call fear is a stress reaction to anything considered dangerous. Fear is having *cold feet, agitation, trepidation*, all with physiological implications.

Fear elicits a series of physiological and anatomical processes aimed at the best possible solution for survival. For a puppy there are several available alternatives, such as retreating, whining, or lying down and yelping. Fear usually leads to flight or immobility and sometimes to displacement behaviour.

Fear is probably innate, for it is vital to the survival of the individual. The first time an animal shows fear-elicited behaviour depends greatly on species-typical behaviour. However, showing immobility, flight, and/or vocal distress, are common features between different species.

A silhouette resembling a hawk, when moved at a certain speed above the nests of ducklings and goslings, elicits fear behaviour when moved in one direction, but not in the other. Hawks have short necks and long tails, while flying geese have long necks and short tails. The experiment suggests that some animals have an innate image of danger and are therefore able to show fear behaviour without previous learning.

However, most young learn vital information immediately after birth from direct interaction with one or both parents. Young ducks must quickly learn to identify their parents, and evolution has attained this feat by compelling ducklings to follow the first moving object they see, which coincides with a species-specific departure call. The call is a sign-stimulus, but it is the act of following which triggers the learning.

Is fear behaviour a set of innate responses to sign-stimuli, or programmed learning? The answer is a combination of pre-programmed mapping, with confirmation of the programming after birth by interaction with the environment. The influence of the environment immediately after the birth and its everlasting effect is what we call *imprinting*.

Experiments with wolf cubs show that although their period of imprinting is longer than in many species, such as birds, it is just as important. Holding a wolf cub for three minutes a day during the first ten days of its life, makes all the difference in its behaviour towards humans later on.[8] The same applies to domestic dogs, even if it is more flexible. The difference is that we have selected dogs for thousands of years for their sociability. We may assume that they have many genes determining this trait, which allows imprinting for longer, or over several periods. A later round, or rounds, of imprinting also serve to define the species image the individual will use to select an appropriate mate when it matures.

Immediately after birth, fear is connected to unpleasant physical stimuli. Later, it follows a general pattern in the development of the puppy, and other stimuli will elicit fear. To learn about what is unpleasant or dangerous in life is a vital exercise. It may be that experiencing the unpleasant motivates the puppy to act to minimise, or optimise, its stimulation—the psychological trend. We can also say that unpleasant experiences demand energy and all organisms are pre-programmed to save energy. Solving an unpleasant situation releases energy for more vital activities—the ethologic trend.

Aggression

Aggression[9]
1. The initiation of unprovoked hostilities.
2. The launching of attacks.
3. Hostile behaviour

At about four to five weeks of age puppies begin to show the first signs of aggressive behaviour. They engage in conflicts with their litter-mates, they even seek them, and they become more assertive. Unquestionably, their motivation does not seek to minimise stimulation, but rather optimise it.

The problem is, as Lorenz showed in 1963[10] that aggression as generally accepted, is only half the truth. Our ethics dictate that it is wrong *to be ag-*

gressive. There is a great difference between being aggressive and showing aggressive behaviour, and there is an enormous discrepancy between showing unprovoked aggressive behaviour and retaliation, following provocation.

These first disputes between pups are very similar to those seen in solitary or non-social predators like the fox. At this stage of their development pups or wolf cubs are not yet social animals. To be social means to *become* social.

All new-born animals are selfish. When they grow up they may lose some of this egoism, and become social. We have invented a word to describe this peculiar aspect of social existence: *altruism*. It means *unselfish concern for the welfare of others*.

The idea of *altruism* is interesting and may give us a clue to understanding why aggression is necessary to be social. In a crude sense, showing altruistic behaviour means to exhibit selfish behaviour in a more sophisticated form— not in the pursuit of immediate advantage, but of long-term benefit. It is likely this has to be learned, but it can only be learned where there is a genetic disposition for it. Certain coat colours in canids and other animals do not show at birth, but develop later. Social behaviour could have the same gene-anatomy.

Altruism can be a mutual-aid system. The 'I help you now, you help me later' principle is a mechanism central to human society. Such a system requires that an animal is able to recognise another as an individual. For the system to work properly, those that accept favours without paying them back must be rejected. This is a valuable clue to understanding the anatomy of social behaviour.

Aggressive behaviour is predominantly motivated by the appearance of a conspecific, because they are the fiercest competitors for the same basic resources.

• Aggression is the ability to show aggressive behaviour, to attack.

• Aggression is a drive triggered by competition, usually by a conspecific.

• Aggressive behaviour aims at resolving or assisting conflicts.

We observe fighting between conspecifics in practically all vertebrate species. Fish nip each other; birds attack one another; cats scratch and bite each other; rats kick and bite; sheep butt their heads together. They fight as their genes have programmed them to. They fight because they find themselves in direct competition over food, mates, and dwelling spaces.

However, male wolves or dogs may fight fiercely, yet they do not usually harm each other. Most intraspecific aggression happens in this way. Such conflict rarely results in significant bodily harm, especially in social animals, where the weighting of the pros and cons of having to live with conspecifics falls in favour of the social benefits.

Animals sometimes direct aggressive behaviour towards members of another species. The cause is still the same, competition or danger to the organism. Or is it? Are there really two types of aggression: (1) interspecific aggression, the conflict between members of different species; and (2) intraspecific aggression between conspecifics?

Some behaviourists sub-divide interspecific aggression into: *competitive aggression*, and *defensive aggression*. Interspecific aggression can, in their view, also be seen as *predatory aggression.*

Competitive aggression is the result of different species competing over the same resources, such as food or water. Lions and spotted hyenas are fierce rivals. They fight mercilessly whenever their paths cross. They do not treat members of other species much differently from the way they treat their own. Lions and hyenas are both aggressive animals which suffer high mortality rates within their own groups. The price for being aggressive and social is high, but evolution can obviously afford to pay it.

Defensive aggression is the behaviour of the animal under attack—a sort of retaliation. The comments which apply to *competitive aggression* also apply to this type of aggression. Aggression is always defensive in one sense or another.

Predatory aggression, towards prey, aims at obtaining food—which is not compatible with the definition of aggression. It does not make any sense to speak of aggression *towards a source of energy*—food.

The ontogeny of aggression

There are three crucial circumstances to explain the ontogeny of aggression in canids: competition with siblings, weaning, and the father (supposing they live in a normal pack).

Puppies meet the urge for aggression for the first time over trivial items, such as a bone. They fight with each other and, without knowing it, they are having their first lessons in how to become social animals. Soon, they realise that they cannot handle siblings by means of aggression and fear and then other strategies begin to appear.

All this happens simultaneously with the pup's mother denying them the best and cheapest source of energy they ever will have; suckling. The time where goods are free is coming to an end, all too prematurely in their minds. Every time they see their mother they try to suckle and sometimes, if they join forces and catch her by surprise, they succeed. Perhaps this is the first sign of active co-operation among puppies. Alone they have no chance. The mother will seize them by the nose, pin them to the ground, growl at them and they will run away, whining and howling.

At roughly the same time, they meet their father, or another adult male member of the pack for the first time. It is usually the first association they have with a complete stranger. Until then, they have only met their mother and siblings. Initially, the father is tolerant and complaisant. He is tender but also strong and awe inspiring. No doubt the puppies fear him at first. They run away whining, as they did from their mother during weaning.

This is a crucial period in the development of the pup's social behaviour. In our domestic environment, pups of 8-12 weeks old are likely to exchange the dog pack for a human pack, and at this time they may learn, as children do, that aggression can enable them to control resources. It has been proved that children whose parents discipline them with physical force tend to use more physical aggression when interacting with others. Research also shows that pups disciplined by tough males show tough behaviour more often than others brought up by a benevolent male.

Everybody competes for a place under the sun: food, sexual partners and territory, undoubtedly the three most important resources for most organisms. Like fear, aggression is a reaction to a potentially endangering situation. An opponent is always a danger unless you control him or her.

Limiting aggression

Fighting involves a certain amount of risk and can lead to serious injury, or even death. Evolution therefore shows a tendency towards developing mechanisms which restrain the intensity of aggressive behaviour.

One of these mechanisms is a genetically programmed tendency to establish *territories*.

Males typically compete for territories, either fighting actual battles or performing ritual combats as tests of strength. This is probably an evolutionary purposeful distribution of labour. Females *generate* the offspring, either by laying an egg or carrying the young inside their bodies; males take care of appropriate nesting sites to maximise the chances of the offspring's survival. Territoriality serves as a mechanism to distribute resources favouring the fittest, and to limit the reproduction of those that are less fit.

The *ritualisation* of aggressive behaviour is another genetically programmed restraint on combat. Bulls scrape the ground with their hoofs, lizards expand a skin fold in their throats, chimpanzees shake branches and shout, wolves and dogs snarl and assume a larger-than-life appearance. The advantage of ritualisation is that all parties save energy.

Most species have clear signals that indicate acceptance of defeat which terminates combat before injury occurs. For example, lizards crouch, while dogs lie down, exposing their throats and bellies. Generally, the more social the species is, the more refined these mechanisms become. Among the species with extremely well-developed aggression inhibition systems are the dog, and its ancestor, the wolf, but how do they learn them?

Puppies play by tumbling around and biting one another. Suddenly one of them gets a grip on another's ear. It bites hard and the poor brother or sister howls in pain. The other puppy succeeds in getting its teeth in the tender skin of its sibling's belly. Much whining and yelling follow. They stand still for a short while, then let go.

Next time they act slightly differently. One will grasp the other's ear only until the puppy begins making noise. It will react to the sibling's vocal distress, which works as a mechanism to inhibit or control aggressive behaviour. Previous experiences showed the puppy it is better to let go at the first signs of vocal distress, or its belly will hurt. This is learning by trial and error.

Visualise another situation. The female is chewing a bone. The puppy wanders up. She gives a warning growl. The puppy ignores it and continues towards the bone. Ten inches from the bone the mother jumps like a flash, seizes the puppy by the muzzle and pins it to the ground.

The pup whimpers and runs away. Ten minutes later the same situation arises. This time, the mother growls and the puppy immediately comes to a halt. It licks the air with its tongue, twisting its hind leg out to the side and waving one front paw. This is what we call *pacifying behaviour* because it has the effect of terminating the opponent's aggressive behaviour.

Pacifying behaviours are patterns previously used for other functions. All these functions have aspects of pleasure in common. The puppy is displaying the same movements that used to bring the good things of life. The licking is associated with suckling, the leg twist with the mother licking its belly and the pawing with the stimulation of milk production.

Although totally unaware, the pup has had its first lesson in ritualised behaviour. The female is teaching her offspring how to compromise — how to survive when 'sometimes you get your own way, and sometimes you don't.

Imagine a litter of wolf cubs coming out of the den. They see the alpha male, probably their father, 10-15 yards away. They run to him and nuzzle him, trying to lick his lips and simultaneously performing the characteristic leg twist. They flop down in front of him, belly up, and then quickly stand up again to follow him and repeat the whole procedure. The father growls slightly. After some time he will seize them by the muzzle, as their mother did during weaning. They lie down voluntarily when he grasps them. Then, satisfied, they will leave the old male in peace, running off to play with one another or a yearling wolf.

The male wolf does not teach the cubs to fear him. [11] Ideally, they want him to regurgitate some food, but if this is not possible they will go for acceptance. It is interesting that these two behavioural traits are so closely linked. In simple terms, the puppies want the male to demonstrate that he accepts them and will not harm them. It is an exercise in self-control which they provoke him to use— 'show us you can grab us without harming us. Show us your self-control.' A male can fail this exercise in two ways: either by ignoring them, or by hurting them. An adult which ignores puppies is a waste of energy for the young: no food, no contact. A violent adult is life threatening.

Social animals spend vast amounts of time together and conflicts are inevitable. It is therefore sensible for them to develop mechanisms with which they can deal with hostilities.

In the long run it would be too dangerous and too exhausting to constantly recur to the great drives to solve banal problems. Animals under constant threat, or constantly needing to attack others, show signs of pathological stress after a time. This suggests that social predators need mechanisms other than aggression and fear to solve social animosities.

It is my suggestion that social animals, through the ontogeny of aggression and fear, develop two other motivational factors.

If the meaning of aggression is 'go away, drop dead, never bother me again', the meaning of *social-aggression* is 'go away, but not too far, or too long'. Equally, *social-fear* says, 'I won't bother you if you do not hurt me,' while *existential-fear* does not allow any compromise—'It's you or me.'

The significant difference between the two types of aggressive behaviour seems to depend on whether the opponent are *aliens*—animals which do not live together and do not depend on one another for survival, or *familiars*—animals which live together and depend on each other for survival. Aggression deals with the *alien* and social-aggression with the *familiar*.

It is the change in motivation that leads us to the creation of these two new concepts. Social-aggression and social-fear show conflict behaviour. Appeasement behaviour shows conflicting intentions. As an example, the wolf cub alternately increases and decreases its distance from the alpha male. More importantly, ritualisations often involve a change in motivation.

A classic example of a change in motivation is courtship behaviour. Initially, the female shows aggression. The male reacts with juvenile behaviour such as *play-face* and *play-bow*. Then it is the turn of the female to show displays of juvenile behaviour. Next, both dogs wrestle for a while and it is only then that the female allows the male to make a tentative mounting. After much tussling, the female allows the male to mount her without moving away.

In the process of ritualisation, behaviour displays change because motivation changes. The signals lose their original function and gain a new meaning.

Social aggression and fear

Social-aggression and social-fear deal with situations *here and now*. The aim of social-aggression is to exercise most influence or control, to have first priority. Therefore we call it *dominance*.

Dominance [12]
1. Exercise of most influence or control.
2. Most prominent.
Dominance is supremacy, ascendancy, pre-eminency.

Social-fear, on the other hand, aims at solving a threatening situation by surrendering. We therefore call it *submission*.

Submission [12]
1. To yield or surrender oneself to the will or authority of another.
2. To allow oneself to be subjected to something.
Submission means: surrender, concession, giving in.

From this point onwards, I shall only operate with the four main motivators of social behaviour to explain all agonistic interactions:

• *Aggression* is a drive directed to the elimination of competition.

• *Fear* is the drive that motivates the individual to react to a threat.

• *Dominance* is a drive directed towards the elimination of competition from a familiar.

• *Submission* is the drive that motivates the individual to react to a threat by a familiar.

Dominance and submission

Dominance is a term widely used to explain animal as well as human behaviour. As we have seen, dominance is social-aggression, which does not aim to destroy the competitor, but control it.

Dominance usually relates to a high status. Dominant individuals have a high status or rank, and a subordinate a low status or rank. The terms *rank* and *hierarchy* are therefore used to explain social interactions in a pack of dogs or wolves.

In dogs, rank orders are for the most part formed by aggressive disputes. If one wins a fight, then the combat may not happen on subsequent occasions, instead the defeated individual is likely to show immediate submission. This depends on the ability to identify and recognise individuals within the pack. It is for this reason that Lorenz claimed aggression is a necessary premise for the creation of individual bonds. [13] The more aggressive an animal is, the more vital it is to recognise other group members in order to be able to show due submission when necessary.

How many encounters are necessary to establish a dominance-submission relationship depends on many factors: the species, the individuals, resources available, the constitution of the group and the environment.

Hierarchies work because a subordinate will often move away, showing typical pacifying behaviour, without any obvious signs of fear. Thus, the dominant animal may simply displace a subordinate when feeding or at a desirable site. Hierarchies in nature are often very subtle and this is the *raison d'être* of dominance-submission itself: the subordinate animal generally avoids encounters, although the dominant one is not too keen on running into skirmishes either.

The strategy of submission is wise. Instead of vainly engaging in a desperate fight, waiting may prove to be much more rewarding. By employing appeasement and submissive behaviour, subordinates are often able to shadow dominant animals and profit from opportunities to gain access to vital resources. By showing submission, they also gain advantages from the membership of the group— particularly defence against rivals.

Dominance-submission relationships are established by learning. Some species show immediate outward signs of dominance. In domestic fowl, dominant males are normally larger and have a more prominent comb than subordinates, and vice versa. Hormones affect the anatomical signs of dominance, which in turn affect the animal's rank. For example, female dogs oppressed by a very dominant alpha female may not come into heat.

The evolution of social behaviour

Fear, aggression, submission and dominance determine the behaviour of social canids. These four mechanisms originated during evolution because they proved to be the best strategy at particular times. It is difficult to prove the advantages of being social, which means to exchange a certain and immediate advantage for a dubious future reward. Social behaviour may have evolved in various ways.

Kin selection, uncovered by W. D. Hamilton[14] is one option. A widespread form of altruism, an animal performs certain services for the benefit of relatives, as they carry some of the same genes. Kin selection explains the evolution of the behaviour and genetics regulating both population density and the evolution of some sexual behaviour.

However, to maintain a constant-sized population, each pair of animals must, on average, produce two offspring. A tiny deviation from this average for many generations invariably leads to a huge increase or decrease in numbers, with unpredictable consequences. Amazingly, most species maintain a population density which fluctuates between specific perimeters.

There are two ways to explain this: (1) the fertility of individuals rises or falls according to a rise or decline in the density of the population, or (2) the individual's chances of survival depend on the fluctuation of the population density.

Obviously, a huge growth in the population leads to starvation, which decimates it. Also, since such a population will not be so healthy, disease will prevail. It is, though, very seldom that a population increases to such an extent that starvation regulates it. This is due to special behavioural mechanisms evolved by *group selection*, as Wynne-Edwards [15] puts it. Such behaviour is advantageous to the group, and thus to the species, but not necessarily to the individual.

There are, however, some behaviour patterns which prevent excessive population growth that cannot be explained by means of traditional selection upon individuals, rather than on a group or a species.

We have seen that *territorial behaviour* has an aggression and fear-limiting function, but in many species it also has a population density regulating effect. For example, a male and a female wolf may stroll and hunt together, but will not normally breed unless they occupy a territory. The wolf pack territory is formed around hunting grounds and the den where cubs are born and spend their infancy. Such behaviour limits population growth because a wolf pack incapable of defending a territory from intruders is probably incapable of breeding or maintaining cubs, too. Aggression, and its regulation by natural selection, determines the size of the wolf pack's territory. Excessively aggressive animals, attempting to defend too large an area, are prone to injury and death and waste too much energy on skirmishes, meaning they are not providing for their young. Excessively shy or fearful animals do not succeed in establishing a territory, or may establish one too small to include an adequate supply of food.

Ultimately, it is the need to establish and control a territory that triggers the evolution of social behaviour, at least in some species. This is yet another reason to develop submission and dominance. If an animal resolves inter-group conflicts with aggression and fear, it may be exhausted when subsequently compelled to expel an intruder from its territory. Thus the *alien* and *familiar* strategy originated and evolved. It is impossible to fight everybody all the time, so a familiar is confronted using energy-saving procedures. Submission and dominance also control population density, since they rely on individual recognition. The number of personal recognitions an animal is capable of must have a limit. If this number exceeds a certain level it makes recognition inefficient, switching off the familiar/alien strategy; fear/aggression displays then replace submission/dominance behaviour.

It is therefore perfectly conceivable that *dominance* and *submission* originated as an evolutionary necessity. These mechanisms probably offer the only viable way to establish an evolutionarily stable strategy for highly aggressive social animals.

Sexual behaviour

Among the various interactions between social animals, sexual behaviour is one of the most interesting, since it usually includes displays rich in ritualised behaviour. Sexual behaviour may therefore give us some insight into the evolution of social behaviour.

To attain its goal, sexual behaviour must ensure that an individual:
(1) mates with a member of its own, and not of a related, species.
(2) mates, or increases the frequency with which it mates.
(3) mates with a specific partner rather than one chosen at random.

(1) As we have seen, the choice of potential mating partners in many species occurs as a secondary round of imprinting, after the learning of primary life-saving sign-stimuli has taken place.

(2) The selection of traits which increase an individual's chances to mate have a large impact on their repertoire of social displays. These traits must be effective, or a great deal of the genetic information of the organism will disappear.

Sexual behaviour is obviously a social interaction. Male and female must tolerate one another, without injuring or killing each other. This seems obvious, and yet many males of different species mate at their peril. Courtship behaviour has evolved to elicit sexual motivation, rather than aggression from the partner.

Polygamy (where a male mates several females) is the main cause of the development of elaborate sexual behaviour. Polygamy is more common than *polyandry* (where a female mates with several males) because a female can only lay a limited number of eggs, or carry a limited amount of progeny inside her body. Males, however, can increase the number of their offspring by mating with as many females as is practically possible.

Dogs and wolves are carnivores, and in principle monogamous. Since they are *social* carnivores, all members of the group help feed the young.

Polygamy is common in ungulates, such as cattle or deer, where the young depend either on their mother's milk or on plants they collect. There is little a male ungulate can do to increase its offspring's chances of survival. Natural selection has therefore emphasised characteristics such as size, horns, and antlers, which enhance the male ungulate's chances of mating with several females. In carnivores however, the difference in size or weaponry between male and female is minimal.

(3) The third aspect of sexual selection relates to the specific choice of partner and was described by Darwin in 1859. [16] The goal is to choose the best possible mate. A good mate is one that is very fertile and likely to increase the chances of survival of his progeny.

The mechanisms involved in choosing a partner reflect what it means to be social, rather than aggressive or fearful. Even in species where partners only meet for a limited time to copulate, specific courtship behaviour has evolved. Most of this behaviour is ritualised. To appreciate the importance of sexual behaviour in canids we need to understand some fundamental mechanisms determining the behaviour of animals.

Darwin pointed out that although a male with striking sexual characters may be the first to find a mate, this will not increase the fitness of his genes, unless it also ensures that he will mate with a female equally fit as a parent. The same applies to females, who need to select males fit as parents, and not only for their masculine features. In other words, in a monogamous species, secondary sexual characteristics, such as 'masculinity', are only favoured by selection if (a) they appear in individuals fitter than the average as parents, and (b) those individuals are able to find mates that are also fit as parents.

In Darwin's view, an association between *secondary sexual characteristics* and *fitness as a parent* must exist, since both characterise the healthiest individuals in a population.

There is no proof that female canids choose their partners on the basis of secondary sexual characteristics, such as body size or ferocity, or the lack of it. However, there is a tendency towards a choice based on rank. [17] Generally, alpha females choose alpha males. By choosing the alpha male, selection also favours other features. To be the alpha, a wolf has to show particular behaviours to maintain its rank with the least possible waste of energy. This means mastering the mechanisms of dominance and submission. Thus dominance and submission behaviours become secondary sexual characteristics which females favour.

This is one point where our selection of breeding animals in domestic dogs can prove detrimental. We choose the sire and dam according to certain aesthetic standards, or learned patterns of behaviour. We never test our dogs for their parental abilities, the ability to provide for their progeny, or how good they are at performing the rituals that natural selection originally favoured. If these abilities were the cause of secondary sexual traits, as for instance the ability to show dominance and submission, we are indeed selecting incorrectly.

A question of conformity

There is great confusion over the use of the terms dominance and submission. Some modern animal behaviourists combine terms at random: dominance aggression, fear aggression, predatory aggression, submissive aggression, territorial aggression, etc.

Such behaviour patterns are not necessarily motivated by these drives. It is not, for example, possible to be fearful and aggressive and the same time. Fear leads to passivity or flight, and aggression to attack. One cannot be immobile and attack simultaneously, or attack under flight. When people speak of fear-aggression they mean submissive-aggression, which may occur when an aggressor does not accept the animal's submission and there is no possibility of escape. The initial submission turns into submission and fear, and finally into submission and aggression. When a dog attacks another it is *always* aggressive.

The idea of dominance-aggression is biased as well. It is possible to be aggressive and dominant, but the term suggests the dog attacks because it is dominant. This is contradictory. Dominance aims at *controlling* another by means of *ritualised behaviour,* without harming or injuring it. A final attack is motivated by aggression alone.

However, it is my opinion that the classification of dog behaviour is meaningless and damaging. For instance, saying that a dog is a fear-biter, i.e. shows fear-aggression, is equivalent to saying that the dog does not behave purposefully and is showing pathological behaviour. By rephrasing the verdict and saying that the dog shows *submissive-aggression* we simultaneously answer the question of how to solve the problem. The dog is submissive, which means reacting to a threat by another, giving in, surrendering. It only becomes aggressive because its behaviour does not have the desired effect. The dog is then under threat and ready to react by flight or immobility. If flight is not possible, it may freeze. Some do and die. Others resort to their last defence, they attack, and then the drive of aggression takes over. This situation is avoided by accepting the dog's submission or allowing it to flee.

Eventually, the young social predator masters the use of the four main mechanisms, their sign-stimuli and behavioural displays, combined with a rich variety of expressions. They are masters of the mechanisms that prevent them wasting time or energy in unnecessary displays. Social predators live in a world where energy is necessary for survival and where waste is heavy penalised. Only the fittest will survive long enough to give their genes to their offspring. Among these highly aggressive social predators the fittest are undoubtedly the best in using the mechanisms of dominance and submission, and their offspring will be even better at using them.

Conclusion

1. *Motivation* is what compels an animal to do what it does.

2. A *drive* is a force, an urge onward, a basic need, a compulsive energy.

3. *Fear* is the drive that motivates the individual to react to an incoming threat.

A *threat* is everything that may harm an individual, or decrease its chances of survival.

Fear elicits flight, immobility or distress behaviour.

4. *Aggression* is a drive directed towards the elimination of competition.

Fighting involves risk. Evolution has developed mechanisms to restrain the intensity of aggressive behaviour. One of these mechanisms is a genetically programmed tendency to establish *territories*.

The *ritualisation* of aggressive behaviour is another genetically programmed restraint during conflict.

A *hierarchy* or *rank-order* is a dominance-submission relationship established and maintained by means of ritualised behaviour.

5. *Dominance-submission* mechanisms limit the use of aggression or fear, thus diminishing conflicts that might decrease the individual's chances of survival.

Dominance and submission originated as an evolutionary necessity. They establish an *evolutionarily stable strategy* for highly aggressive social animals.

Dominance and submission behaviours evolved partially as *secondary sexual characteristics.*

Dominance, or *social-aggression,* is a drive directed towards the elimination of competition from a familiar.

Familiars are two or more animals who live closely together and depend on one another for survival.

Aliens are two animals who do not live closely together and do not depend on one another for survival.

Social-aggression usually elicits ritualised aggressive behaviour, where a familiar is not injured. It may consist of body postures, facial and vocal expressions.

Submission, or *social-fear*, is the drive that motivates the individual to react to a *social-threat* from a familiar.

A *social-threat* is everything that may cause submissive behaviour or flight, without the individual being harmed.

Social-fear usually elicits submissive behaviour following the familiar's threat or flight. It may also elicit vocal distress or displacement activity.

Final note

The cells of an organism transform energy, maintain their identity, and reproduce. A life form is dependent on many thousands of simultaneous and precisely regulated metabolic reactions to support them. Specific cell enzymes control each of these reactions and their co-ordination with numerous other reactions in the organism—this applies to all life, from single-celled algae to human beings!

Barely 14,000 years ago we were predators on a par with our soul brother, the wolf. We too are highly aggressive animals, with sophisticated rituals and inhibition mechanisms, the most peculiar and refined of all being language.

Recent discoveries have shown that the learning of human language is partially a kind of imprinting. Three-day-old babies recognise consonants as sign-stimuli and can discriminate between sounds in their own language and those of foreign ones. Maybe human and animal behaviour are two sides of the same evolutionary coin after all.

Notes

1. The American Heritage Concise Dictionary, *Houghton Mifflin Company 1994.*
The Oxford Thesaurus, *Oxford University Press, 1991.*
2. Darwin, C. (1859) On The Origin Of Species By Means Of Natural Selection, Or The Preservation Of Favoured Races In The Struggle For Life. (1872) — The Expression Of The Emotions in Man and Animals.
3. Watson, J.B. (1924) Behaviorism, *New York, The Norton Library.*
Skinner, B.F. (1938) The Behaviorism of Organisms, *New York, Appleton-Century-Crofts.*

4. Lorenz, K. (1965) Evolution and Modification of Behaviour, *The Univ. of Chicago Press.*

— The Foundations of Ethology, *New York, Springer-Verlag.* (1981). Tinbergen, N. (1951) The study of Instinct, *Oxford University Press.* Frisch, K. von. (1965) Tanzsprache und Orientierung der Bienen, *Heidelberg, Springer Verlag.*

5. Maynard Smith, J. (1958) The Theory of Evolution, *Penguin Books England.*

Dawkins, R. (1976) The Selfish Gene, *Oxford University Press.*

6. Peirce, C. S. (1958) Selected Writings, *London, Constable and Co.*

7. The American Heritage Concise Dictionary, *Houghton Mifflin Company 1994.* The Oxford Thesaurus, *Oxford University Press, 1991.*

8. Christiansen, F. W. & Rothausen, B. (1983) Behaviour Patterns Inside and Around The Den Of A Captive Wolf Pack, *Lungholm Wolf Research Station, Denmark.*

9. The American Heritage Concise Dictionary, *Houghton Mifflin Company 1994.* The Oxford Thesaurus, *Oxford University Press, 1991.*

10. Lorenz, K. (1963) *op. cit.*

11. Christiansen, F. W. & Rothausen, B. (1983) *op. cit.*

12. The American Heritage Concise Dictionary, Houghton Mifflin Company 1994.

The Oxford Thesaurus, Oxford University Press 1991.

Microsoft Encarta, Microsoft Corporation and Funk & Wagnall's Corporation 1994.

13. Lorenz, K. (1963) *op. cit.*

14. Hamilton, W. D. (1964) The Genetical Theory of Natural Selection, *J. Theoretical Biology 7, (I)1-16, (2) 17-32.*

15. Wynne-Edwards, V.C. (1962) *op. cit.*

16. Darwin, C. (1859) *op. cit.*

17. Mech, L.D. (1970), The Wolf: The Ecology And Behavior off An Endangered Species. *New York, The Natural History Press.*

Zimen, E. (1981), *op. cit.*

Abnormal behaviour

Abnormal behaviour is all behaviour that quantitatively differs from the average behaviour of a certain species, breed and population, in a certain geographic region and in a certain period of time.

The difference between abnormal and pathological behaviour is that the latter involves greater qualitative differences, while abnormal behaviour is an exaggeration of the norm. For example, if a dog shows extreme aggression every time it sees another dog of the same sex, it is showing abnormal behaviour. However, this behaviour is not likely to be pathological unless it is due to hormonal or organic changes in the brain.

NORMAL BEHAVIOUR, PATHOLOGICAL BEHAVIOUR.

Acoustic communication

See **Sound signals.**

Active submission

See **Submission**.

Aggression

The word aggression often carries negative connotations. The word is usually associated with struggle and violence. Yet according to some scientists, aggression is what makes personal relationships possible—it's the basis for friendship and love.

Aggression is a drive—purposeful energy—which is aroused by meeting with a conspecific. Conspecifics compete over vital resources like food, territory and sexual partners. It is of great importance for animals to have certain mechanisms with which they can control others. Aggression is the drive behind the initial desire of one individual to kill another, or preferably chase it away. Encounters between individuals of many species occur in this way. For example, a tiger cub's worst enemy, besides a human, is an adult male tiger, which may even be their own father.

However, other animals have realised that they need help from conspecifics to survive. This is not a product of an individual's consciousness, but occurs at a species level—the fittest under specific circumstances is the survivor. For example, it is difficult for a lone wolf to get food for itself, but if there are two of them they significantly increase the chance of acquiring food, if there are three they can begin hunting systematically. In some species, selection favours those individuals who are best at inhibiting their aggression and co-operate instead. This does not mean aggression disappears, rather it assumes other forms through ritualised behaviour: greeting ceremonies, pacifying behaviour and rank ordering. Instead of killing each other, the animals engage in ritualised behaviour where they display some of the original aggression without damaging each other.

Animals which have learned to ritualise their aggression still have a need for it though, such as when they meet strangers. A wolf pack cannot grow unreservedly. While members of a small group have a better chance of acquiring food than a lone wolf, a huge pack would contradict its own interests. This means that wolves are very keen to chase non-pack members away.

Very aggressive animals need to know each other individually. For example, it could be a fatal mistake to attack a superior conspecific more than once. The rituals that two individuals perform are unique to both, and thus they come to know each other. Other animals that live in groups, like rats, do not know each other individually — they only know whether or not they belong to the same group. Rats lack the rituals we see among other animals such as wolves, dogs, geese, chimpanzees and humans.

Aggression does not only lead to agonistic behaviour; it is the reason for the bond between individuals. How aggressive a species or population is is determined by selection. In a society where all individuals are aggressive, a peaceful mutant will have greater chances of survival since it will not fight with others as often as aggressive individuals. In a population of peaceful individuals, an aggressive mutant will have a better chance, since it will win all the fights it has. The quantity or the lack of aggression in a population is a result of many factors, all concerned with self-preservation. No animal is

Aggression is shown by means of facial expressions. The three illustrations in the upper row show both aggression and dominance. Dominance is highest to the left and lowest to the right. The wolf in the middle is aggressive and awaiting, i.e. neither dominant nor submissive. The three wolves in the bottom row show aggression and submission. The one at the bottom left is very aggressive and very submissive. Notice the position of eyes, ears, forehead and lips—they tell us of the wolf's dominance and submission status.

only aggressive and no animal is totally devoid of aggression. Aggression is a quantitative trait, depending on the benefits for that individual under specific circumstances. The individual that has the greatest chance of survival also has the greatest chance to mate successfully and have offspring that will inherit 50 per cent of its traits.

The aggressive dog bares its teeth. If it is dominant as well, i.e. self-confident, it will have raised ears, curled lips, a well-defined stop, staring eyes and will make its body appear large and stiff. If it is submissive, i.e. insecure, it will flatten its ears, draw back its lips, flatten its forehead and narrow its eyes. It will crouch to make its body appear as small as possible and may creep along the ground. How obvious these signals are and when they are shown together depends on circumstances, rank order and so on.

Aggression is not a disease, but it can be the cause of pathological behaviour. If an individual shows aggression which has qualitative and/or quantitative differences from the average for that species and population in a certain period of time, it can be considered abnormal behaviour. Certain dogs show exaggerated aggression in situations where other dogs would be unresponsive. If we don't treat this behaviour in good time it can develop into pathological behaviour. Aggression may then be elicited by factors which wouldn't normally result in such behaviour.

Aggression varies in intensity and this can be seen clearly in the dog's facial and bodily expressions.

AGONISTIC BEHAVIOUR, FEAR, DOMINANCE, SUBMISSION, DRIVE, RITUALS, SOCIAL ANIMALS, GREETING, SELECTION, PATHOLOGICAL BEHAVIOUR.

Aggression and submission. When submission is not accepted and flight is impossible, wolf and dog will fight back.

Aggression to children

See **Children and dogs**.

Aggression to dogs and humans

It is normal for a dog to look at strangers with suspicion until greeting ceremonies have assured it of the opponent's peaceful intentions. However, it is abnormal to attack every human or dog encountered, and this can be due to several factors: inheritance, imprinting, early learning, a lack of leader role from the owner, and illness.

Dog owners are advised to teach their puppies to accept people, dogs and other animals as early as possible. For years there has been discussion about the dangers of socialising puppies from eight weeks of age because of the risks of infection with various diseases, such as canine hepatitis, distemper or parvovirus. However, recent advances in veterinary science have produced vaccines which can be used very early on with satisfactory results, enabling dog owners to socialise their puppies from eight weeks of age. The possible consequences of inadequate socialisation at this age are, in my opinion, far more serious than the risk of illness. Contact your veterinary surgeon for more information on this subject.

If a dog shows aggression to humans or dogs encountered on a walk, owners should take immediate action, though not using violence. Much aggressive behaviour in such circumstances is not meant seriously by the dog, but is a result of a bad habit, tolerated by the owner. Both owner and dog should change their behaviour immediately.

Never buy a puppy if the parents show high levels of aggression towards people or dogs.

AGGRESSION, GREETING, INHERITED BEHAVIOUR, LEADERSHIP, PATHOLOGICAL BEHAVIOUR.

Aggression to other animals

True aggression is only seen towards conspecifics. When a dog runs after a cat it is not motivated by aggression, but by the hunting instinct and the drive of self-preservation. The term *predatory aggression* is not an accurate use of the word aggression. The act of chasing prey demands deep concentration and the use of specific faculties concerned with determination and self-preservation—no behaviour patterns normally seen in agonistic encounters with conspecifics are observed. While true aggression aims at getting rid of the opponent, not necessarily killing it, predatory behaviour aims at exactly the opposite—the predator needs to kill the prey in order to eat it.

Attacks on other animals may be due to exaggerated possessiveness over territory or the owner. Some dogs also show very strong possessiveness over items like bones, sticks and toys. Dogs can be taught to live peacefully with other animals as long as they accept the leadership of their owners in the *family pack*.

AGGRESSION, SOCIAL ANIMALS, DRIVE, TERRITORY, LEADERSHIP.

Agonistic behaviour

Agonistic behaviour (Greek agon = struggle, fight) is all forms of aggression, threat, fear, pacifying behaviour, fight or flight, arising from confrontations between individuals of the same species. Many of the dog's expressions are a result of the conflicts or interactions between different forms of agonistic behaviour.

AGGRESSION, FEAR, PACIFYING BEHAVIOUR, FIGHTING, FLIGHT, THREAT, TERRITORIAL BEHAVIOUR, DEFENSIVE BEHAVIOUR, ATTACK.

Agoraphobia

Agoraphobia (Greek agora = place of assembly, market place) is a morbid dread of public places or open spaces. Many animals have inborn agoraphobia, which has a self-preservation effect. Young dogs may show slight signs of agoraphobia in that they prefer sheltered places, rather than wide open spaces. For example, puppies prefer a little box to sleep in rather than the big basket that many pet shops try to sell to new owners. Dogs have to learn to be confident in wide open spaces, in public and amongst strangers, although many breeds have been selected for their inborn ability to show a high degree of this trait.

Dogs who show agoraphobia are cautious in their movements: they walk slowly with their legs crouched under them and with their necks extended to detect possible scents of danger. The more agoraphobic the dog, the more obvious these postures become.

CLAUSTROPHOBIA, PATHOLOGICAL BEHAVIOUR, FEAR.

Attack and flight are both forms of agonistic behaviour.

Allelomimetic behaviour

Allelomimetic behaviour is contagious behaviour, i.e. behaviour which influences another to do the same.

Dogs commonly show allelomimetic behaviour. It is often advantageous for social animals to display this sort of behaviour. In prey animals like deer, zebra or wildebeest, one individual has the ability to trigger the whole herd

When a wolf or two begin howling they will very probably be answered by several other wolves—contagious behaviour is also called allelomimetic behaviour.

to flee. This trait is so important for self-preservation that farm animals like sheep, cows and horses still retain it. Social predators show these traits for hunting purposes. If one member of the pack suddenly runs after possible prey it is likely to trigger the same response in the whole pack. The wolf's howl may also be considered allelomimetic. When one wolf begins howling, the whole pack joins in in chorus, especially if a high-ranking wolf has initiated it.

Dogs clearly show allelomimetic behaviour when they bark because the neighbour's dog is barking, or when they run after playing children.

IMITATION, SOCIAL ANIMALS, HOWL.

Alpha

See Leadership, Rank order and Rank ordering.

Altricial animal

An animal is described as altricial if it requires parental care and feeding in order to survive after birth.

Altruism

Altruism means unselfishness, the regard for others as a principle—the opposite of egoism or selfishness.

It is doubtful whether animals show altruistic behaviour, since the concept itself is unclear. If by altruism we mean that the individual may not get anything at all in return for its actions, then it is questionable whether altruism exists at all. However, this definition does not take into account the self-satisfaction that always seems to follow an altruistic act. If we define altruism as unselfish behaviour in the short term, i.e. without immediate advantage, we are able to find many more examples of such behaviour. Parental behaviour is typical. Mothers and fathers do a great deal for their offspring without immediate advantage to themselves. The female dog spends a lot of time and energy looking after her puppies, teaching them various skills and feeding them. She regurgitates for them and will defend them if they are in danger.

Some theories regard altruistic behaviour as a genetically selfish behaviour. When parents sacrifice themselves for their offspring they are benefiting themselves, in as much as their offspring possess 50 per cent of their own genes. For example, in a wolf pack it pays the father or mother to sacrifice their own life to save three of their puppies, since this means saving three times 50 per cent of their own genes. The calculation is more complicated if we take into account the chances of the cubs' survival without the parents' influence. If the cubs are one week old, it doesn't pay for the parents to give up their lives to save them, since the cubs are unlikely to survive. In this instance, the best strategy is for the parents to save themselves and retain the possibility of having more offspring later. This theory also explains why individuals sacrifice more for their own offspring than for those of relatives or strangers.

EGOISM, MATERNAL BEHAVIOUR, PATERNAL BEHAVIOUR.

Anal glands

Anal glands are two internal glands near the anus. They produce a substance which is secreted with faeces. This substance smells offensive to humans.

In extreme or sudden situations of fear the dog will empty its anal glands. This cannot be ignored by the human nose, and certainly not by the dog's much better sense of smell. Anal gland secretions probably have an identity-giving function, for instance, when territory marking, but there is little conclusive evidence to confirm this theory.

MARKING, DEFECATION, TERRITORIAL BEHAVIOUR.

Anthropomorphism

Anthropomorphism (Greek *anthropos* = human and *morph* = form) means to attribute human characteristics and intentions to animals. In scientific approaches we must beware of anthropomorphism which can lead to misunderstandings of animal behaviour and the formulation of incorrect hypotheses.

Dog owners are often likely to give their dogs human characteristics and motives, such as jealousy, guilt, premeditation and so on. These lack any kinds of factual basis.

COMPARISON, JEALOUSY, CONSCIENCE.

Appearance

See **Phenotype** and **Genotype.**

Association

Association is a process involved in learning. Some authors use the concept

Some dogs associate the behaviour of the owner when going out with the following lonesome period. Then they may begin showing signs of fear prematurely.

of association in connection with conditional learning, initially studied by Pavlov and Skinner. Other authors are of the opinion that association and conditional learning are two different processes, association being a more conscious process of the mind.

Association may lead to fear and aggression as well as psychosomatic behaviour such as emptying the anal glands, scratching and self-mutilation. Since the dog's language is not the same as ours, with abstract concepts, semantics and so on, we have to be very careful when attributing abilities of association to the dog, which it cannot comprehend. For instance, we should not scold a dog if we come home and realise it has soiled the house. It may have happened some hours previously and the dog certainly does not associate the scolding with its earlier behaviour.

LEARNING THEORIES, CONDITIONED BEHAVIOUR, PSYCHO-SOMATIC BEHAVIOUR, MEMORY.

Attack

Attack and threat are closely connected. Much of the dog's attack behaviour is really pseudo-attack, where the dog threatens the opponent without touching it. These attacks are governed by aggression mechanisms, inhibitions and pacifying behaviour, all with very clear modes of expression. Some attacks happen without warning, these are called uninhibited attacks and normally arise from rank-ordering disputes between individuals who have had serious conflicts over a period of time. Attack without threat under other circumstances is considered abnormal or pathological behaviour. A predator chasing prey cannot be regarded as mounting an attack, since hunting behaviour is not triggered by aggression, but by hunger.

When seizing prey, wolf and dog show concentration and agility. When attacking another wolf or dog they show signs of aggression and dominance or submission in various degrees.

THREAT, PACIFYING BEHAVIOUR, INHIBITIONS, NORMAL BE-HAVIOUR, ABNORMAL BEHAVIOUR, PATHOLOGICAL BEHA-VIOUR, DOMINANCE, SUBMISSION, TAIL.

The attacking wolf (right) is aggressive and dominant. The defensive wolf (left) is aggressive and submissive.

Back

A taut, straight back means self-confidence, dominance. A hunched, bowed back is associated with insecurity or submissive behaviour. Both patterns are shown in connection with many other body signals.

Dogs sometimes circle before lying down. This manoeuvres the spine to allow it to curl up, protecting its belly and snout against wind and cold.

The back assumes various positions according to the dog's gait.

MOVEMENT, BODY LANGUAGE, DOMINANCE, SUBMISSION.

Barking

Barking is used by the dog as a rough means of communication, primarily to warn other dogs about intruders. In our homes, dogs bark to warn us of the vicinity or arrival of strangers, and to get our attention. During conflict, submissive dogs bark in more varied tones and with more snarling than dominant individuals. Barking can also be used as an invitation to play or during other social activities involving high arousal. In these cases, barking is more high-pitched and monotonous.

Many breeds of dog bark a lot, and this is caused by selection and learning. When man domesticated the dog there was an obvious advantage in favouring barking dogs since this trait made them very effective as guards. Much barking in our modern society is caused by under-stimulation—the dog barks because it has no other outlet for its pent-up energy. Dogs often bark against the wishes of their owners who didn't manage to stop them at the onset of the problem. This problem is one of the most common complaints from owners about their dog's behaviour.

SOUND SIGNALS.

Behaviour

Behaviour means a way of acting. Everything in the way the individual appears to others is counted as behaviour. There is no precise scientific definition of the concept of behaviour. For instance, there is disagreement whether some ways of acting should be classed as behaviour, depending on whether the actions are conscious or subconscious. Language is behaviour, in as much as it communicates intention, emotion and affects others' behaviour.

BEHAVIOUR THEORIES, LANGUAGE.

Behaviour theories

Ethologists have explained behaviour in many different ways. We build models to understand the behaviour of living beings. No model is perfect, partly because of the difficulty in defining behaviour precisely.

Behaviour biologists put emphasis on biological factors and explain behaviour in terms of the living organism's functions and purposes.

Behaviour physiologists underline physiological processes. Behaviour is the visible result of the relation between different chemical processes that the organism undergoes.

Behaviour ecologists explain behaviour by means of environmental factors and the adaptation of organisms to it. Changes in the environment imply changes in behaviour, since survival requires adaptation.

The theory of instinct explains behaviour as a series of instinctive displays. The ability to perform certain behavioural sequences is inborn. When certain stimuli are present the animal acts as it is programmed to.

SR (Stimulus Response) theory sees behaviour as responses to certain stimuli. Certain responses do not need previous learning, or conditioning, while others require it. This is the difference between unconditioned and conditioned reflexes.

The theory of motivation puts emphasis on initiating factors: anger, fear or aggression motivate the animal to hunt, flee, or fight. The greatest motivational factors are *drives*: self-preservation, aggression and reproduction. Among other factors, drives use instincts to fulfil their requirements and satisfy their needs.

HISTORY OF ETHOLOGY, BEHAVIOUR, CONDITIONED BEHAVIOUR, DRIVE, INSTINCT.

Biotonus

Biotonus (Greek bios = life, tonus = force).

See **Vitality.**

Bite

To bite is to grip with the teeth. Dogs use their mouths to grip items, but this is not generally referred to as a bite—a bite is an aggressive act where one dog grasps another with the intention of harming it.

Dog owners should not encourage their dogs to grip humans with their teeth. Many aggression problems originate from owners having indulged in rough play with a puppy, allowing it to bite.

Bites are normally preceded by a warning such as a growl or snarl. However, uninhibited attacks are usually not preceded by such a warning.

AGGRESSION, SNARL, GROWL, INHIBITIONS.

Bite inhibition

Bite inhibition is the behaviour displayed by a dog when it does not bite an opponent although it would be easy for it to do so. In a situation like this, most dogs will limit themselves to grasping or mouthing the opponent without causing damage. When the opponent shows passive submission, the healthy, well-balanced dog limits itself to snarling close to the other's belly and throat without biting. Inhibition mechanisms play a major role in interactions between aggressive social animals— preventing damage and death during conflict. Healthy dogs show distinctive bite inhibition mechanisms. If conflicts cannot be solved by displays of dominance or submission, individuals may then fight. Sometimes fights are fast and furious and yet no damage occurs. Inhibition mechanisms regulate rank ordering disputes. Wolves only show uninhibited attacks when they want to force an opponent to leave the pack, such as when the alpha female is in heat and wants to get rid of direct competitors.

INHIBITIONS, BITE.

Both wolves have small eyes. The wolf to the right may eventually blink a little. This means friendliness and submission.

Blinking

When a dog blinks it shows friendliness or submission. The alpha wolf or the leader of the pack may accept the submissive individual's greetings by blinking. This means that it accepts the other's greeting and offers a calm response. The submissive dog blinks in return and licks its lips and champs, which means friendliness and submission.

Dogs often blink at humans, for example, when they have been too harsh or seem aggressive.

FACE, EYES, INFANTILE BEHAVIOUR.

Body

Since the body is everything from the head to the tail, information about the signals given by different parts of the body are listed under each part's heading.

The body as a whole reflects the motivation of the animal. Darwin mentioned that an animal which is aggressive and self-confident makes its body as large as possible, and the opposite is true for an animal which is fearful and lacking self-confidence. Wolves and certain dog breeds may make the hair on their head and neck stand up when they are showing self-confidence in the preliminary stages of a confrontation. Raising the hackles is a similar mechanism. The dog which is fearful and submissive tries to hide. It cringes and keeps the head low.

BODY LANGUAGE, AGGRESSION, FEAR, DOMINANCE, SUBMISSION.

Body contact

There are two types of body contact. The first fulfils a basic need: puppies keep close to each other and to their mother to share warmth and security. It has been shown that animals without this sense of safety do not thrive and may even die.

The other type of body contact is used for communication. A muzzle-nudge, where one dog butts another or our hands with its muzzle, is a ritualised behaviour which means friendliness. The hip-nudge means friendliness in dog language, as well. A muzzle-nudge to the neck shows acceptance of the other's superiority.

Body contact is not only vital for young animals, where their survival may depend on it, but is also important for adults. Two dogs who live together often lie close, touching each other. Dogs like to lie on their owners' feet, and to have close company. This is obvious when we realise that the dog is a pack animal with a vast genetic programme for co-operation. Body contact also strengthens the tie between individuals. Owners of more than two dogs know that it is not accidental which dog likes to lie with which. Dogs seldom show such intimate behaviour towards strangers or humans.

Body contact may be used as a demonstration of dominance, such as when an older dog puts his head over a young dog's neck while it is lying down.

Much of the behaviour involving body contact has its origins in infantile behaviour.

INFANTILE BEHAVIOUR, NURSERY BEHAVIOUR, MATERNAL BE-HAVIOUR, PARENTAL CARE, NEONATAL BEHAVIOUR.

Body control

Control over the body, agility, and the ability to balance, are indispensable skills for a wolf. Cubs begin exercising these techniques from an early age. A fallen tree may be used to climb on and practise balancing. A ditch can be used to practise jumping. All these activities teach the cub about its own capabilities and prepare it for adult life where it is vital to be able to cope with the environment.

Our puppies show the same curiosity and also learn from their early experiences. Dog owners should give their puppies as much chance as possible to develop their body control.

Body control activities have been proved to have a therapeutic use for hyperactive dogs. Such dogs may become more settled with the help of balance

Learning about the environment—body control is often more important than pure physical strength. Cubs and pups train regularly their sense of balance. Body control activities have been proved to have a therapeutic use for hyperactive dogs.

exercises and controlled physical activities, rather than by means of explosive exercise, like running and jumping.

Body language

Body language means all the signals that one animal transmits to another by means of one or several specific parts of the body, or its entire appearance. In order that these signals can be regarded as communication, they must deliberately change the receiver's behaviour.

The dog uses all parts of its body to give information, but particularly its head and eyes, teeth, lips, ears, eyebrows, and various wrinkles. The throat and neck, with their many possible angles and combinations usually confirm other signals. The legs and the torso are mostly used in simple communication.

The tail has a clear language all of its own. Dogs with docked tails, or tails which we have altered dramatically from their original form for aesthetic reasons, may seem handicapped when trying to communicate. It's very common to see dogs with docked tails wagging with their entire rear ends to compensate.

The dog's understanding of its own species' detailed body language enables it to read human body language as well. Signal-sensitive dogs which are liable to translate human body language into dog language may react differently than expected in certain situations. For example, the human greeting of bending forward, with out-stretched hand and smiling—which involves showing the teeth—may be regarded as dominance and a threat by the signal-sensitive dog.

Generally, dogs are more likely to register visual signals than auditory ones and this may be useful to remember in training situations.

AGGRESSION, FEAR, DOMINANCE, SUBMISSION, PACIFYING BEHAVIOUR, FRIENDLINESS, TAIL LANGUAGE.

Boredom

See **Under-stimulation.**

Brain

The brain is composed of nerve cells conducting electrical impulses called *nerve impulses*. The brain is divided into the forebrain, midbrain and hindbrain. The forebrain is furthermore divided into the interbrain and endbrain. These divisions are clearly seen in the embryo. The size of the brain has nothing to do with how intelligent the animal is—the elephant has a brain much larger than ours, but it cannot be said to be more intelligent. However, we can compare animals of different species which are the same size, by looking at the volume of the brain which is needed to control the activities of the body and how much is left over for other activities.

The brain's ability to solve problems and decide on purposeful and intelligent strategies is determined by the number of cells and the number of connections between them used to perform a certain action. The function of the heart and breathing are regulated by the hindbrain. Sleep and wakefulness are regulated by the *formatio reticularis*, which is found in the hindbrain and midbrain. Eating and drinking are controlled by the hypothalamus in the interbrain. Sexual behaviour is also influenced by the hypothalamus and a gland situated nearby, the pituitary gland. During stress reactions, such as fear, it is normally the sympathetic system which mobilises the resources leading to action and the parasympathetic which conserves body resources and maintains routine functions. Both systems belong to the autonomic nervous system. By triggering the relevant brain centres, we can force the animal to act in a specific way; to sleep, build nests, eat, or show aggressive behaviour. Interestingly, laboratory animals whose brain centres are triggered in this way only show behaviour which is normal for that species. For example, the animal won't try to build a nest unless nesting material is available and it won't display aggressive behaviour towards an individual that it earlier feared.

In the *neo-cortex*, there are parts with specific functions. The more developed the animal is, the more neo-cortex there is in relation to the total size of the brain. In small insect-eating animals the neo-cortex is approximately 30 per cent of the brain, in contrast to 75 per cent in chimpanzees and 80 per cent in humans. Some parts of the neo-cortex need a great deal of physical space. The amount of space necessary is dependent on the animal in question. For instance, primates have large areas concerned with visual information, and carnivores greater areas for the reception and processing of auditory information. The areas for associative functions vary greatly from species to species, and are apparently linked to the ability to learn. Experiments have shown that the removal of the *association cortex* influences an animal's ability to learn. A special area of the association cortex deals with forgetting or disregarding previously learned patterns. Damage to this area reduces the animal's ability to change an earlier learnt behaviour pattern.

In spite of similarities between the human brain and the brains of other animals, there is a crucial difference. In the human brain there are areas which enable the development of language, i.e. the ability to describe the world around and the self. There are two speech areas called the *Broca's* and *Wernicke's* areas. The Broca's area deals with talking, and Wernicke's area with the ability to understand what is said. If these areas are damaged, the ability to understand and be understood by others is reduced.

The differences between animals' brains and their structure is a result of evolution. Evolution established two main strategies: some animals have brains which enable them to produce stereotypical actions with great precision. These animals are highly efficient in their natural habitat, but have great difficulty in dealing with sudden changes. In captivity some of them show abnormal behaviours or passivity. Other animals have brains which give them better learning abilities. They can learn from association between earlier experiences and the result of previous actions. These animals are less effective in their performance of specialised actions, but are more adept at dealing with sudden changes in their natural habitat: they are more adaptable.

The brain is a complex organ and we still know too little about it. With the help of the electron microscope we can see cells and the connections between them, but the number of connections is still too great for us to have an overview of the fundamental processes. There is no doubt that animal behaviour is dependent on the functions of the brain. Ultimately, the brain is a

When a dog is tired, stressed, or fearful, its rate of breathing increases.

product of genetic information collected through a centuries-long struggle for survival, and perfected through selection forced by environmental changes.

BEHAVIOUR THEORIES, GENETICS, EVOLUTION.

Breathing

When a dog is tired, stressed, or fearful, its rate of breathing increases. Stress increases the rate of breathing to bring more oxygen to the lungs.

STRESS.

Breed

A breed is a group of individuals of a certain species which have a high percentage of common inherited characteristics, or in other words, they have many common genes.

BREED DIFFERENCES.

Breed differences

Breed differences arise from selective breeding; by choosing individuals with specific characteristics. After a number of generations the new population differs from the original ancestors. This difference may be phenotypic, e.g. size, coat colour, and genotypic.

Basic behaviours like dealing with self-preservation and sexual behaviour are common for all breeds. Most differences show themselves in anatomical traits: ears, tails, or snouts, all with varied forms. Some of these traits have influence on the dog's behaviour. For example, the shape of the ears may lead the dog to be more or less acoustically oriented. We have also selected dogs according to their abilities, such as hunting or herding. Some have been selected as sled dogs and others for our protection. Our selection has shaped the behaviour of different breeds as well as learning capacities, need of contact, and other more basic behaviours.

Some people believe that certain breeds cannot learn certain skills, but this is not entirely true. In principle, all dogs can learn the same skills. The problem is that some breeds need greater motivation to learn some skills and others do not. It is easier to teach a Cocker Spaniel to retrieve than a Yorkshire Terrier. A German Shepherd finds it easier to learn a recall than a Siberian Husky. A Border Collie has a natural herding ability, but an Estrela Mountain Dog can learn it as well. The difference is in the degree of motivation we have to use and in the amount of training. Of course, there are some skills which are impossible to teach certain breeds for obvious reasons. For example, it might prove a bit difficult to teach a Chihuahua to retrieve a fox!

Siberian Husky. close to the wolf in anatomy.

The German Shepherd with longer ears and going down in the hind legs.

There are many dog breeds. They were created through selective breeding and mutations.

The Collie with its peculiar ears and long muzzle.

The Golden Retriever with the ears turning down.

The Cocker Spaniel, smaller and with even longer ears.

The Fox Terrier with its peculiar ears, raised tail and stiff movements.

The Dachshund has extremely short legs.

The Basset hound has even shorts legs compared to the body and extremely long ears.

The Boxer has a characteristic flat snout.

The Old English Sheepdog has the longest coat among all dog breeds.

The Pekingese has a record breaking flat nose and the tail over its back.

Canidae

See **The Canine family.**

Canine

Canine (Latin caninus, canis = dog) means of, or as of, a dog or dogs. The canine teeth are the four big pointed teeth between the incisors and molars.

Canine Family — The

Animals are placed in the zoological system depending on similarities. Systematic studies resulting in the ordering of animals in various groups, classes, orders and so on have been very important for our understanding of animals' evolution, their way of living and their needs. These studies have undoubtedly contributed to a greater understanding of our own role in a world full of other living forms.

Our dogs are placed in the zoological system as follows *(illustrations pages 68-69):*

Group *Chordata* — animals with a spinal cord.
Row *Vetebrata* — animals with a backbone.
Class *Mammalia* — mammals.
Order *Carnivora* — carnivores.
Sub-order *Fissipedia* — land-living carnivores.
Over family *Canoidea* — land-living carnivores which, among other differences, cannot retract their claws.
Family *Canidae* — dog-like animals. The characteristics of the family are well-developed limbs, pads under the paws, five toes, one of them not reaching the ground, strong necks, well-developed claws, no collar bone (clavicula) and well developed senses, especially the olfactory sense. The teeth have the following form:

Upper row	3	1	4	2
Bottom row	3	1	4	3
	incisors	canine teeth	pre-molars	molars

In the sub-family Caninae there are the following species:

Canis adustus — Side-striped jackal.

Canis aureus — Golden jackal.

Canis mesomelas — Black-backed jackal. All jackals live in Africa. They live in small family groups.

Canis familiaris — the domestic dog, descended from the wolf. Some breeds originated from cross-breeding with wild-living dogs. Dogs can have offspring when crossed with wolves, coyotes and jackals. Some figures say there are over one thousand dog breeds across the world.

Canis familiaris dingo — the dingo, the wild dog from Australia.

Canis latrans — coyote, which lives in North America and Canada.

Canis lupus — the wolf; the Grey, Timber or European wolf. The Grey wolf is the largest of the Canidae family, with a shoulder height of some 60-80 centimetres and weighing up to 50 kilograms. The wolf is a threatened species. Free-living wolves can be found in North America, Canada, Russia, Eastern Europe, Italy, Spain and Portugal, and a few in northern Scandinavia. There are probably 38 variations of the Grey wolf.

Canis niger (also called *Canis rufus*) — the Red wolf. This wolf is under great threat on North America's east coast.

Canis simensis — the Abyssinian wolf from Ethiopia, sometimes called the Abyssinian fox.

Alopex lagopus — the Arctic fox, living in the Arctic regions.

Atelcynus microtis — the Small-eared fox, from South America.

Cerdocyon thous — Crab-eating fox, from South America.

Chrysocyon brachyurus — the Maned wolf. South America.

Dasycyon hagenbecki — the wolf from the Andes mountains. South America.

Dusicyon — six (or eight) species of fox-like animals living in South America.

Fennecus zerda — the Desert fox, (the Fennec fox) lives in North Africa, the Sahara.

Nyctereutes procyonoides — a racoon-like dog from east Asia, Japan and North Europe.

Urocyon cinereoargenteus — the Grey fox. North America.

Sub-family Otocyoninae

Otocyon megalotis — the Bat-eared fox. South and east Africa.

Vulpes bengalensis — the Bengal fox. Asia.

Vulpes cana — the Blandford fox. Afghanistan and Iran.

Vulpes chama — the Chama or Cape fox. South Africa.

Vulpes corsac — the Corsac fox. Asia.

Vulpes ferrilata — the Tibetan sand fox. Afghanistan, Iran.
Vulpes macrotis, (Vulpes velox) — the Kit fox of North America, (nine varieties).
Vulpes pallida — the Pale fox, or African sand fox. North Africa.
Vulpes rupelli — the Sand fox, or Ruppell's fox. North Africa.
Vulpes vulpes — the Red fox. There are about 50 varieties in Europe and North America.

Sub-family *Symnocyoninae*. This family is distinguished from the Caninae by the formula of the teeth. (Molars 1—2/1—2)

Cuon alpinus — the Asiatic Wild, Red or Dhole dog. There are ten variations in central and eastern Asia.
Lycaon pictus — the African or Cape Hunting dog. Africa.
Speothos venaticus — the South American Bush dog, from Brazil.

Canis

(Latin = dog). See **The Canine family.**

Cannibalism

Cannibalism is the act of eating an individual of the same species. The occurrence of cannibalism is influenced by over-population, availability of food, the behaviour of the victim, and stress. Cannibalism may influence the structure of a population and is regulated by the rules of natural selection.

Carnivores are not more likely to be cannibalistic than others and it does occur in canids, but only rarely. When it does happen, it is mostly as passive cannibalism, i.e. the individual that is eaten was already dead.

EVOLUTION.

Carnivore

Carnivore (Latin caro or carnis = flesh, carnivorus = meat eater).

See **The Canine family.**

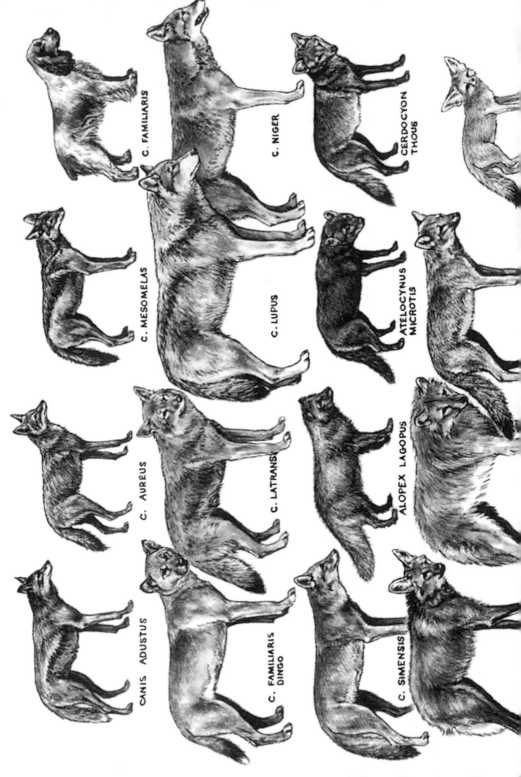

C. FAMILIARIS

C. NIGER

CERDOCYON THOUS

C. MESOMELAS

C. LUPUS

ATELOCYNUS MICROTIS

C. AUREUS

C. LATRANS

ALOPEX LAGOPUS

CANIS ADUSTUS

C. FAMILIARIS DINGO

C. SIMENSIS

The Canine Fami

VULPES BENGALENSIS

V. FERRILATA

V. RUPPELLI

SPEOTHOS VENATICUS

UROCYON CINEREOARGENTEUS

V. CORSAC

LYCAON PICTUS

OTOCYON MEGALOTIS

V. CHAMA

V. PALLIDA

CUON ALPINUS

NYCTEREUTES PROCYONOIDES

V. CANA

V. MACROTIS

V. VULPES

Champing

Champing is a noisy chewing motion, despite there being nothing to chew. This behaviour is connected with friendliness, pacifying of an opponent, insecurity, or submission depending on the degree and context. Champing is one of the first sounds that puppies hear—when their siblings suckle. It is therefore a sound connected with satisfaction. Redirection of the champing behaviour later means pacifying behaviour—trying to turn an unpleasant situation into a pleasant one. Champing is originally connected with the appeasement of hunger.

Champing is a simple and effective way to show friendliness towards a dog. In fact, this behaviour appears to have a relaxing effect on most mammals.

GREETING, PEOPLE AND DOGS, REDIRECTED BEHAVIOUR, NEONATAL BEHAVIOUR.

Children and dogs

Many misunderstandings between child and dog end tragically, with the child being bitten. Commonly, the dog is rehomed or destroyed. The child may have physical or emotional scars for the rest of his or her life.

Problems between children and dogs have to be taken extremely seriously and preventative measures should be put into action immediately. When a child is bitten by a dog it is always the adults' responsibility. If a child and a dog misunderstand each other so blatantly, it is because we have failed. We haven't been effective enough in explaining to the child how dogs understand our behaviour and we certainly have been irresponsible dog owners, as we should have taught the dog to always and absolutely respect a child and never touch him or her. Apologies and explanations are useless after the event. A child must never pay the price for a dog owner's ignorance.

Even if the dog owner is not a parent, and is not planning to be, he or she must teach their dog to accept children and to behave properly in their presence. We should regard every child as our own and our most important task is to protect them all. A bitten child is a mark of shame for all dog owners. Take particular care over the following situations:

The dog must never be allowed to pick up the child's toys in its mouth. If this happens, instruct the child not to try to take the toy from the dog, but to tell you, or another adult.

Do not allow dog and child to play football, where tackles with unforeseen consequences are unavoidable.

Instruct the child not to run in the dog's presence, as this is liable to encourage the dog to chase the child.

Discourage all attempts by the dog to jump up at the child, as this frightens most children.

Do not allow child and dog to sleep together. This intimacy could be misunderstood by the dog and result in dominant behaviour towards the child. It can also result in the development of an allergic response from the child.

Never feed the dog and child together. The vicinity of food is a factor likely to trigger extra awareness in the dog and possibly result in dominance or aggression.

Instruct the child about the fundamental principles of understanding the dog, so that teasing and similar behaviour can be avoided.

Always show respect for all animals and life. It is my experience that children reflect their parents' attitudes in an astonishingly high number of cases. However, children can be extraordinarily good at understanding and training dogs if they have good teachers. Experiments conducted at the Etologisk Institut concluded that children are significantly quicker than adults when teaching dogs new tricks. They are also better at reinforcing certain behaviour patterns.

MISUNDERSTANDINGS BETWEEN PEOPLE AND DOGS.

Chromosomes

Chromosomes (Greek, Khroma = colour, soma = body) are thread-like structures occurring in pairs in the nucleus of cells. They carry the genes, genetic information which is responsible for inherited characteristics, and chromatin which can readily be stained in the laboratory—hence the name chromosome.

The domestic dog (*Canis familiaris*) has 78 chromosomes: 38 pairs plus X and Y, like the wolf, (*Canis lupus*) and the jackal (*Canis aureus*). The number of chromosomes for canids (*Canidae*) varies from 34 to 78.

Only animals with the same number of chromosomes can breed together successfully. A wolf and a dog can have healthy offspring, whereas a dog and a fox (*Vulpes vulpes*) cannot.

GENETICS, GENE, DNA.

Classical conditioning

Classical conditioning is the learning process where an unlearned stimulus is connected with a learned stimulus to elicit the same response —a learned or conditioned response. In classical conditioning as Pavlov and Skinner describe it, the sight of food is paired with a flashing light to elicit salivation, then the flashing light alone is shown after several repetitions, and salivation occurs.

A reflex is said to be unconditioned when an unconditioned stimulus elicits an unconditioned response. Unconditioned reflexes are unlearned. They are inborn, such as closing your eyes when something approaches them at speed. Many unconditioned reflexes have life-saving functions.

A conditioned reflex is comprised of a conditioned stimulus eliciting a conditioned response. This is learned.

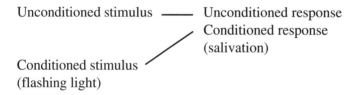

Unconditioned stimulus —— Unconditioned response
Conditioned response
(salivation)
Conditioned stimulus
(flashing light)

The following rules must be observed under conditioning:
1. The stimulus to be conditioned must be neutral before conditioning.
2. The conditioned and unconditioned stimulus must be presented together repeatedly.

3. The conditioned stimulus must be presented together with the unconditioned stimulus. It may be presented a little before, but never after.

4. After a period of time where the conditioned and unconditioned stimulus are not presented together, conditioning is again necessary.

We must distinguish between stimulus and stimulus object. In Pavlov's example, the stimulus is the flashing of the light and the stimulus object is the bulb.

LEARNING THEORIES, STIMULUS, RESPONSE , REFLEX, CONDITIONED BEHAVIOUR, STIMULUS OBJECT.

Claustrophobia

Claustrophobia (Latin, claustrum = enclosed place, phobia = fear) is the fear of being in confined places.

Dogs may show apprehension when going into unknown confined or dark places. Claustrophobia is not usually the cause of the problem for dogs that cannot be left at home alone—these dogs are usually fearful of being alone or are under-stimulated.

Dogs suffering from true claustrophobia are very rare, as opposed to those which suffer from agoraphobia, which is a more common problem.

AGORAPHOBIA, FEAR, PATHOLOGICAL BEHAVIOUR, UNDER-STIMULATION.

Co-operation

The question whether animals co-operate or not is difficult to answer, since there is not a single, clear definition of what co-operation is. Whether dogs and wolves co-operate to solve certain problems such as hunting, or just perform their actions together, is unclear.

Some observations seem to indicate that co-operation does take place. During hunting, wolves are very attentive to each other's behaviour and they often change course in response to the actions of another wolf. Yet at other times they may look more like a third division football team, where each one is trying to get the ball into the goal without any form of plan, or any co-operation.

Co-operation certainly seems to occur when taking care of youngsters. Adult wolves take care of the cubs, protect them and carry food home to the den.

SOCIAL ANIMALS.

Colour

Wolves and other wild canids, as well as many dog breeds, show a variety of combinations in head markings based on the grey spectrum. Facial expressions are no doubt emphasised by nuances in coat colour.

There is no conclusive research showing that dogs cannot see colour, even if it is normally assumed that dogs can only see in black and white. Dogs have better vision at night than humans, probably indicating that they have more rods than cones in their eyes. This does not exclude the possibility of seeing colour, but makes the black and white theory more probable.

COLOUR VISION, HEAD MARKINGS, FACIAL EXPRESSIONS.

Colour vision

Colour is a strange phenomenon. If we put a white screen in the path of refracted light from a glass prism, a band of colours called a spectrum is formed. Light and colour are perceived by the eye with receptors— the rods and the cones. The rods facilitate vision at night and in low light intensity and the cones are responsible for vision during the day and for colour vision, which requires light to be fully appreciated.

In many species, colour plays a very important role in the identification of individuals, such as in mating ceremonies, choice of partner and other displays of social behaviour. In dogs, colour does not seem to play a significant role, but grey tones seem to be important.

COLOUR, HEAD MARKINGS.

Communication

Communication and language are commonly associated with each other. We often overlook information given by facial expressions, body signals and touch. These expressions are subconscious and yet for the attentive observer they may emphasise, confirm or deny what the spoken words express. Humans are the only living beings on earth which have developed such a complex and abstract communication system as language. Communication does not need to be comprised of an interchange of words as we understand it. In the animal world where words do not exist, communication is still possible and indispensable.

Is all behaviour communication? If I scratch my head, the behaviour in itself is not communication, but if someone else changes his or her behaviour because he or she observes me scratching, then we are taking about communication. This leads us to the following definition: when an animal does something which causes another to change its behaviour, and this is not accidental, then they are communicating.

Communication presupposes at least three factors: a sender, a receiver and a signal. Signals are received through the senses of sight, hearing, touch, taste and smell. Signals may be facial expressions, barking, licking, or chemical substances, such as the urine of a female in heat.

Many signals are ritualised behaviour. Behaviour is said to be ritualised when it has lost its original function and has obtained a meaning. For example, the behaviour of puppies seeking their mother's teats, with the characteristic upwards movements of the head, becomes ritualised to mean friendliness and appeasement through the muzzle-nudge. The greater part of the signals used by human and animal to communicate are ritualised behaviour traits which originally had a certain function, but not the later meaning.

Dogs communicate by using all their senses. Sight plays a very important role. Dogs communicate by means of facial expression and body posture, which are visual signals. Barking, snarling, howling and other vocal expressions are used to give basic or general information. It is through facial and body expressions that dogs explain in detail to each other what they want, what they do not want, what their intentions are, and maybe even their mood.

Examples of communication in dogs:

Behaviour	Sense receiving the signal	Meaning
Wrinkling the nose (snarling)	Sight	Aggression
Raised ears	Sight	Dominance
Deep sound (growling)	Hearing	Aggression
Long, high pitched sound (howl)	Hearing	Loneliness etc.
Muzzle-nudge	Touch	Friendliness
Scent marking (urine)	Smell	Territorial claim
Scent marking (urine)	Smell/taste*	Female in heat

*See Jacobson's organ.

BEHAVIOUR, FACIAL EXPRESSIONS, BODY LANGUAGE, BARKING, HOWL, SNARL, GROWL, AGGRESSION, FEAR, DOMINANCE, SUBMISSION, VOCAL LANGUAGE, SCENT, SCENT SIGNALS, RITUAL.

Comparison

To compare means to find likenesses or differences, to match, to parallel. Comparison is an indispensable means of studying animal behaviour and it is used in all natural sciences. Unknown patterns of behaviour in one species may well be unravelled by comparing them with that of another. (See illustration page 78).

However, when using a comparative method one must beware of becoming anthropomorphic.

ANTHROPOMORPHISM.

Conditioned behaviour

There are two ways to condition behaviour: either by classical conditioning, first described by Pavlov, where there is an association between stimulus and response, or by operant conditioning, as described by Skinner, when an association occurs between a certain response and a reinforcement.

It is possible to teach dogs to behave in certain ways by using classical conditioning, although generally speaking this is only practical for very simple traits. More complicated traits or behaviour sequences need to be taught through operant conditioning and shaping.

Certain fearful or aggressive responses may be a consequence of classical conditioning.

LEARNING THEORIES, STIMULUS, RESPONSE, REFLEX, OPERANT CONDITIONING, SHAPING.

Conscience

Whether animals have a conscience is impossible to know, since there is no way to verify it.

When an owner describes his dog as showing clear signs of having a guilty conscience—after it has been destructive, for example, this is not a correct definition from an ethological point of view. It is more likely that the owner's behaviour elicits the dog's submissive and perhaps fearful behaviour, which is mistakenly assumed to be a conscience. Dogs are very perceptive. For example, if an owner expects their dog to be destructive while they are out, it is likely that the dog will appear to look guilty as soon as they come

To compare means to check for likenesses or differences, to match, to parallel. The three illustrations above all show pacifying behaviour—these are the similarities. The human displays greeting behaviour, i.e. friendliness, the chimpanzee shows fear and the dog submission—these are the differences. All three behaviour patterns have one common element: the hand, the paw—earlier connected with the acquisition of food— taking food from an adult's mouth or performing kneading movements.

home. Of course, the dog does not remember it chewed its owner's best shoes three hours earlier, but has learned to anticipate its owner's anger. This is the reason why punishment after the event has absolutely no effect, and may even exacerbate the problem.

Contagious behaviour

See **Allelomimetic behaviour.**

Contradictory behaviour

Contradictory behaviour is all behaviour made up of conflicting signals. For example, a dog which is snarling with raised ears, but with its tail between its legs, is showing contradictory behaviour. The raised ears show dominance, but the tail shows submission.

Contradictory behaviour specifically occurs when the individual is caught between conflicting motivations. However, this is rare. Many behaviour traits which have been explained as being contradictory, are not, on closer investigation. For example, it is not contradictory for a dog to snarl, crouch and simultaneously flatten its ears. The dog is showing aggression and submission at the same time, which are not contradictory forms of behaviour. It would have been contradictory to say that the dog was showing aggression and fear at the same time, as early models did. They explained social behaviour through the exclusive interaction of aggression and fear. In the new model, social behaviour is explained through the interaction of aggression, fear, dominance and submission, giving us several more alternatives to explain apparently contradictory behaviours.

During courtship, females often seem to behave in a contradictory way. They show a certain degree of aggression, but are simultaneously inviting. They do not intend to chase the male away as they normally would if motivated by aggression.

Some authors describe some forms of pathological behaviour as contradictory behaviour. For example, a dog which bites its owner in a moment of panic caused by an unspecified phobia.

AGGRESSION, FEAR, DOMINANCE, SUBMISSION.

Coprophagia

Coprophagia is the behaviour where an animal consumes its own or another animal's faeces. There are many theories as to why some animals do this, but none are truly satisfactory.

It has been suggested that coprophagia is a consequence of curiosity in young animals where they use their mouths to explore the environment. Another theory suggests that the behaviour helps the animal establish specific intestinal flora in the gut, although this has been totally disproved for many species. Another suggestion is that eating faeces compensates for some nutritional deficiency, by utilising the deoxycholic acid present in the waste. Other ideas include stress, pancreatic deficiency, heavy intestinal parasitic loads and even taste.

There is no certain solution to this problem. Many dog owners report that after a period of successfully preventing their dogs from eating faeces, the problem reoccurs time and again.

ABNORMAL BEHAVIOUR.

Cavernous body

See **Tie.**

Courage

Courage means bravery, to risk life and limb, even though there is a low probability for a successful outcome.

Regarded in this way, animals are seldom courageous. Courage contradicts common sense. When it's safest to run away, there's no point in engaging in a hopeless fight. How courageous an animal appears to be in certain situations therefore depends on motivation. If the animal is very hungry it will take more risks than normal to acquire food. Animals show courage when they have to defend their offspring.

The concept of courage as commonly used in competitions and tests of dogs of certain breeds is totally useless. In the end, if the dog's action is not elicited by a strong and valid motivation, what might at first appear to be courage is merely stupidity.

Courtship behaviour

Courtship behaviour is the series of patterns of behaviour shown by the dog before mating. This behaviour includes many aspects of play. Courtship behaviour is an important aspect in mate selection.

See **Sexual behaviour**.

Before mating dogs play as if they were fighting.

Cryptorchidism

Cryptorchidism (Greek, kruptos = hidden, and orchis = testicle) is the dog missing both testicles. In reality it is rare that the dog is without both—they are usually hidden in the groin.

A dog which is only missing one testicle is called a monorchid (Greek, monos = one).

Cryptorchid dogs may be more active than dogs with both testicles. When one or both testicles are situated in regions with higher temperatures than normal, such as when they are retained in the groin, chemical processes are speeded up.

Exaggerated aggression is sometimes a consequence of cryptorchidism.

Tumours may grow in the retained testicle or testicles, causing surgery to be necessary. However, many cryptorchids have been known to live long and peaceful lives.

Cryptorchidism is inherited. However, it is not yet known how this occurs.

HYPERACTIVITY.

Curiosity

Curiosity is a deep desire to gain experiences from the environment. All animals are curious, but their eagerness to investigate new environments and objects diminishes with age. It is difficult to measure and compare curiosity in different age groups or animals of different sexes. Curiosity is closely connected with motivation. An older animal can show curious behaviour in the same way as a young one, provided that it is sufficiently motivated.

Normally, young animals are more curious than older ones. Everything new has to be investigated thoroughly. Young puppies initially sniff at new objects and then grasp them in their mouths and bite them. The purpose of this behaviour is to gain as much knowledge about the objects as possible, including smell, taste and texture. Later, smell is probably the greatest source of identification. Texture and taste obviously have greater importance when puppies are dealing with edible items. All this activity is excellent practise in developing motor skills.

The wolf cub's curiosity ensures it comes into close contact with animals which will later be its prey. The cub's cautious behaviour does not scare the prey away, enabling the cub to gain valuable experience. Obstacles may be overcome and this again contributes to giving the cub a detailed knowledge of its world—a world which it will need not only to master, but also to live in

Normally, young animals are more curious than older ones. Everything new has to be investigated thoroughly. The purpose of this behaviour is to gain as much knowledge about the objects as possible, including smell, taste and texture.

harmony with. Sometimes it is best to attack, at other times it's best to flee, and on other occasions it's best to keep as quiet as possible. Young animals learn all these devices thanks to their inborn curiosity.

INFANTILE BEHAVIOUR.

Cynology

Cynology (Greek, kuon = dog, logos = thought/reason/justification) is the science concerned with the study of dog-like animals, so-called canidae.

THE HISTORY OF CYNOLOGY.

Cynology - The history of

The development of cynology, the study of canine behaviour, has always been dependent on other natural sciences, especially ethology, biology and zoology. Man and dog, or rather man and wolf, probably began co-operating some 14,000 years ago after the last Ice Age. In the beginning, man probably used dogs as guards and hunting companions and then as a sled dog. Later, as sheep and goats were domesticated, the dog was used to herd the flocks. It is only in relatively recent times that the dog has been used for other reasons, such as a police dog, sniffer dog or guide dog.

Man's use of the dog for practical purposes implies that we had a good knowledge of the dog's needs, way of living and behaviour, even 14,000 years ago. However, it is only in the last part of the 20th century that canine studies show relevant scientific results. Paradoxically, this is due to the fact that the dog is now regarded mainly as a companion, rather than a working animal.

In the Fifties, J.P. Scott and J.F. Fuller conducted long and detailed studies to investigate the genetic basis of dog behaviour. By using several breeds and systematically cross-breeding them, they discovered many aspects concerning the inheritance of behaviour. At the same time, C.C. Little wrote a comprehensive study on the genetics of coat colour in the dog.

In the 1960s and 70s, the study of canine behaviour flourished. Michael W. Fox conducted basic studies on the behaviour of different canidae, such as the wolf, jackal, fox and coyote. He also collated the most relevant studies of other scientists. Another aspect of Fox's work is his ethical approach towards animals, a matter that came to the fore much later, in the 1990's.

Wolf researchers A. Murie, D.L. Mech, D.H. Pimlot, R. Schenkel, S.P. Young, and E. Zimen, among others, contributed to a better understanding of wolf behaviour and its ecological place. In doing so, they also contributed to a better understanding of the dog's behaviour and its inheritance from their ancestor the wolf. These studies also succeeded in destroying the myth of the wolf as an evil and malevolent beast.

From the end of the 1970s, Eric Zimen and Dorit Feddersen-Petersen completed a great number of comparative studies between wolf, jackal and dog, and cross-breedings between them. He also studied the behaviour of the wolf in the wild and in captivity.

In the same period, Eberhard Trumler completed in-depth studies of the behaviour genetics of the dog and the dingo. These gave us many details about our domestic dogs' behaviour.

In later years, studies have concentrated on man and dog in our modern society. Projects have shown that dogs may have a therapeutic value for elderly people, children, those receiving psychiatric care and so on. In England, SCAS (Society for Companion Animal Studies) was founded in order to collect knowledge and to study the use of companion animals in our modern world. The Delta society in the US was created for the same reason.

The dog's abnormal or pathological behaviour came into focus in the Eighties. Since Kruschinskii's time we have come a long way towards an insight into pathology. In the United States, Peter Borchelt and Victoria Voith reached many practical conclusions concerning diagnosis and treatment of pathological behaviour in dogs and made the veterinary profession aware of the importance of curing behaviour problems.

Ian Dunbar started as a veterinarian, but became so deeply involved in studies of dog behaviour that he gave up practice to concentrate on spreading knowledge about behaviour therapy programmes, learning theories and training methods compatible with the new ideology which will take us into the 21st century—psychology, instead of power. Dunbar's impact in the US dog training world has had a tremendous effect. The *Association of Pet Dog Trainers,* created by Dunbar, with a completely different approach to training and handling dogs from earlier practice, grows every day, and there is no doubt that its views and methods will dominate the 21st century. The relationship between man and dog has changed forever!

Another vet contributing to the spread of interest and understanding in dog behaviour is Anglo-Canadian Bruce Fogle, through popular quality books.

Roger Mugford founded the Animal Behaviour Centre in 1982, with the purpose of treating behaviour problems in pets. Mugford's methods adhere to a 'never say no' policy, which avoid correcting the dog with the voice. It is Mugford's belief that correction of the dog's unwanted behaviour should not be connected with the owner, but instead with purpose-built devices. He furthermore states that if a dog lives with a very strong and dominant owner it will suffer.

In England, the creation of the APBC (Association of Pet Behaviour Counsellors) by John Fisher, Peter Neville, John Rogerson and David Appleby, was a great advancement in the recognition of behavioural therapy as a science. John Fisher was one of the first in England to make dog owners aware of the beneficial use of food when training dogs. He also pointed out that by forcing the dog we may often achieve the opposite result of what we wanted—in other words, negative thigmotaxis is likely to occur. John Rogerson was already a well-known dog trainer in England when he decided to abandon classical training methods and came up with a series of alternative suggestions for how to solve training problems. Rogerson's ideas are based on the belief that dogs learn by trial and error and the pack structure dictates much of the animal's behaviour. Many of his ideas are based on the premise 'control the games, control the dog'. David Appleby passes on his practical experience in dealing with behavioural problems through the popular press. Valerie O'Farrell is a psychologist of the opinion that the knowledge of the dog's communication patterns and instinctive social behaviour is very important in order to have a good relationship with the dog as a pet. She does not agree with the old saying that there are no bad dogs, only bad owners.

In Scandinavia it was Anders Hallgren who started a revolution in the way of looking at the relationship between ourselves and our dogs as pets, and the treatment of problem behaviour. A great part of Hallgren's methods are based on classic behaviourism, operant conditioning and shaping, combined with an ideology which demonstrates great respect and affection for the pet dog.

Swedes Lars Fält and Sven Järverud contributed to a better understanding of the dog, the former through the study of canine ethology, the latter through training methods.

Since 1980, the Etologisk Institute at the Høng Agriculture School in Denmark, under the scientific supervision of the author, has conducted various projects dedicated to the study of canine behaviour as well as the relationship between dog and man and the treatment of problem behaviour. Britta Rothausen and Freddy Christiansen revealed many aspects of the behaviour of a captive wolf pack—Canis lupus—in and around the den. Ralf Vollstedt did the same project with the fox—Vulpes vulpes. Hanne Hjelmer-Jørgensen dedicated a study to the behaviour of the Greenland Sled Dog. Finally, the author of this book studied the development of social behaviour in canids through the results of all of the above-mentioned projects and put forward a new model for the understanding of this behaviour which can be read in *The Evolution Of Canine Social Behaviour.*

Defecation

Dogs often mark their territories by defecating. Defecation contains odour particles that dogs are able to identify. Some dogs take trouble to defecate in prominent places so that others cannot avoid detecting it. This behaviour is often seen in males, especially dominant ones.

Dogs develop preferences for location and surface for defecation and urination. It is therefore important to teach the dog from puppyhood to get used to specific locations where we want them to urinate and defecate. Dog owners who use the newspaper method to teach house-training often complain about continuing soiling on a periodical basis well into adulthood. Normally, puppies will learn house-training from eight to ten weeks of age until four or five months old.

MARKING, TERRITORIAL BEHAVIOUR, URINE.

Defensive behaviour is a display of aggressive and submissive postures.

Defensive behaviour

Defensive behaviour is a reaction to attack. Defensive behaviour is like flight behaviour, a stress reaction following attack or threat. The difference between the two is that while escaping or fleeing the animal avoids 'the conflict, whereas by assuming defensive behaviour it actively enters the situation, either by avoiding the opponent's attacks or by attacking in return. Defensive behaviour is therefore often a combination of submissive and aggressive behaviour.

When escaping, the animal shows submission and fear. Dogs show defensive behaviour when flight is impossible, except when it defends itself near the centre of its territory, or is a lactating female. In these two cases, defensive behaviour can become very similar to attack, where the dog shows aggression and dominance at the same time.

AGGRESSION, FEAR, DOMINANCE, SUBMISSION, FLIGHT, ATTACK, TERRITORY, TERRITORIAL BEHAVIOUR.

Dialect

When a form of speech is strictly peculiar to a certain location or group of individuals, we call it a dialect. (Greek dialektos = speech.) Whether dogs communicate with dialects is difficult to answer since the dog's communication patterns cannot be classified as language with all its semantic characteristics. Dogs of different breeds use different signals depending on anatomical differences between them. These variations are always variations of basic signals and can hardly be considered as dialects in comparison with dialects in human languages.

LANGUAGE.

Displacement activity

Displacement activity is all activity performed to change the motivation in a given situation, in order to escape. The individual tries to achieve a sense of security by performing an activity which it feels safe with and connects with pleasure.

The most common displacement activity in male dogs is marking territory by urinating. Picking objects up and carrying them is another example of a

Muzzle-nudge in the air is a typical displacement activity.

typical displacement activity, especially in situations where owners pressure their dogs to solve a problem they don't understand. When corrected or reprimanded, dogs often show displacement activity.

Mating movements and other sexual behaviour can also be seen as displacement activities in dogs.

MOUNTING, THRUSTING, PENIS, STRESS.

DNA

DNA (deoxyribonucleic acid) is regarded as the molecule of heredity. DNA is confined to chromosomes. A chromosome is a long strand of DNA coiled on itself. Chromosomes contain genes which carry the information necessary to build organisms with all their varying functions and predispositions.

Dog family

See **The Canine family.**

Domestication

Domestication (Latin, domus = home), is the process whereby a wild animal becomes tame. This process happens by keeping the animal near humans and human habitations and by breeding from the individuals that show greatest social traits towards humans, or are best suited for our objectives.

The dog (canis familiaris) is the domesticated form of the wolf (canis lupus). On average, a dog has 50-80 per cent of the wolf's social behaviour traits, either in their true form or in a slightly modified form.

THE CANINE FAMILY, SELECTION, SELECTIVE BREEDING.

For about 14000 years ago humans and dogs began to interact more closely. They found out that they could cooperate. This was the beginning of the lasting alliance between the two species.

Dominance

The concept of dominance and submission, or superiority and inferiority, are central to the understanding of a social animal's behaviour.

Social animals are animals forced to work together in order to survive. When these animals are aggressive as well—as for example, the wolf, dog and human - rank ordering systems are a solution to the problems of having to live together.

Rank ordering is normally established without bloodshed since all actions which could be damaging decrease the chances of survival and thereby affect selection. Rank ordering is mainly done through ritualised behaviour.

Rank ordering involves aggression and fear and is motivated by these two great mechanisms. However, any social animal which had to resort to aggression and fear to maintain a rank order and solve innumerable daily conflicts would sooner or later become stressed and drained of energy, perhaps even showing neurotic types of behaviour. It is therefore important that young social animals learn very early on to compromise with older conspecifics, which means that they are sometimes forced to submit and sometimes get their own way.

When the female teaches her puppies *dog language* by snarling at them, attacking them and so on, she is not teaching them fear, but rather helping them to find their place in a very specialised ecological system — the wolf pack in its habitat.

Social animals have developed from being motivated uniquely by aggression and fear to show behaviour which is motivated by specialised social factors—dominance and submission, or superiority and inferiority.

Fear and submission follow each other. Behaviours showing fear and submission are therefore very closely related and only differ from each other in small degrees and nuances. Aggression and dominance are also connected with each other and sometimes can only be distinguished from each other by observing degrees of a behaviour pattern instead of the behaviour itself. The difference is that aggression and dominance do not exclude the possibility of other simultaneous motivating factors. A dog can be aggressive and

Dominance is clearly shown through facial and bodily postures.

submissive at the same time. A popular mistake is to see these dogs as aggressive and fearful, which is due to misunderstanding the difference between fear and submission, as well as following early models which do not operate with the concept of submission. When fear and aggression are seen displayed in quick succession we are normally dealing with a pathological behaviour.

The dominant dog shows a self-assured gait, a large, confident body posture, raised head, raised ears, large eyes and curled lips, all in different intensities and combinations depending on the degree of dominance, superiority, or self-confidence.

SUBMISSION, AGGRESSION, FEAR, MATERNAL BEHAVIOUR, RANK ORDER, RANK ORDERING, SOCIAL ANIMALS, SELECTION.

Dreams

Dreaming is subconscious activity during sleep. We cannot tell whether dogs dream in exactly the same way as we do. Sometimes they move their paws as if they are walking and they may snarl, wince and bark. Dog owners shouldn't worry if their dogs dream, as there are no known cases of dogs being harmed by any dreaming activity.

Dribble

Dogs showing fear have a tendency to dribble in excess. Even in situations which would usually elicit fear, dribbling is more likely to be seen in connection with phobias.

Dogs also dribble when tired, hot or car-sick.

FEAR, PHOBIA.

Drive

Drive means compulsive energy. Self-preservation, aggression and sex are drives.

Self-preservation is the energy directed towards survival. This drive governs hunger, thirst and the need for rest.

Aggression is the energy triggered by meeting with a conspecific. Conspecifics are true competitors for important resources such as food, resting places and mating partners.

Sexual drive is energy directed towards mating and reproduction.

We must distinguish between instinct and drive, where instinct is the inborn ability to perform a complete behaviour sequence. For example, it is not mating that causes the animal to show sexual behaviour, but quite the opposite; sex compels the animal to mate and for this purpose it uses the inborn ability to perform the act of mating.

Drives are highly relevant in building communication patterns since they ultimately motivate the individual to act.

SELF-PRESERVATION, AGGRESSION, SEXUAL BEHAVIOUR, MO-TIVATION, INSTINCT.

Ears

When a dog shows dominance it holds its ears erect (unless physical breed characteristics do not allow it). Drawn-back ears show friendliness, submission or fear, depending on the degree of flattening and context.

Ear positions often reflect the motivation of the dog, but the degree to which they are used and the context, dictate that it is always necessary for us to observe other behaviour patterns in order to decide exactly what the position of the ears means.

When a dog greets us or other dogs it normally moves its ears up and down. Most dogs will also move their ears in response to their owner's voice. This is not a sign of changing dominance and submission, only that the dog is attentive.

Dogs with drop or very heavy ears also show the same basic movements as their counterparts, but these may be less obvious.

FACIAL EXPRESSIONS, HEARING.

Raised ears mean self confidence and retracted years insecurity. The position of the years combined with other body postures express various emotions.

Eating

In a wolf society, eating behaviour is influenced by rank. The higher-ranking individuals normally eat first, especially if food is scarce, while lower-ranking members wait their turn. From an evolutionary point of view, this favours the survival of the fittest, resulting in the survival of those individuals' cubs and the perpetuation of their genes. However, actual possession of food, even by the lowest ranking member, is rarely contested by another.

It is normal that minor conflicts arise during feeding of more than one dog—there may be some snarling, but this is usually without further consequences. If problems develop it could be an indication of a deeper incompatibility between the dogs.

HUNGER, RANK ORDER.

Ecology

Ecology (Greek oikos = house, and logi, logos = justification, the science of) is the science that studies the relationship between organisms and the environment. Organisms, living and non-living, are studied in populations and placed in ecosystems. Ecosystems are biological communities and their physical environment. The study of ecosystems is important in the understanding of evolution.

The behaviour of our dogs also needs to be seen in broader perspective in order to be fully understood. The ecosystem in which our dogs live now differs greatly from the ecosystems their ancestors evolved to master. This is frequently the reason for the so called problem-dog.

SELECTION, EVOLUTION.

Egoism

Egoism (Latin, egoismus, ego = I, ismus = action of/practice) is selfishness. An act is said to be egoistic when it is done only for the individual's own benefit. The concept is vague, making it difficult to decide whether animals show egoism, or altruism. Usually, when these concepts are used to describe animal behaviour we are committing the crime of anthropomorphism, which should be avoided in all scientific descriptions of animal behaviour, as well as in explanations of daily situations.

ALTRUISM.

Emotion

Emotions are states of mind, feelings that affect behaviour. The concept is unclear due to the difficulty of describing something which only belongs to the subject who had the experience. A witness can only guess at the emotional experience from the former's behaviour.

Ethologists try to avoid explanation involving the concept of emotion. For example, in a situation where a dog attacks another dog the ethologist does not explain it by saying the first dog is angry, but that the attack probably occurred as a result of what happened in the past. The ethologist tries to describe what can be seen, not what the individual experiences.

Darwin was one of the first scientists to study emotion in animals. For him, there were three main emotions: anger, fear and joy. However, he recognised that more intelligent animals could express more emotions. Darwin was very practical about emotions and explained them by saying they were necessary for animals to see when others were in a hostile mood—and avoid them.

ETHOLOGY — THE HISTORY OF.

Environment

The environment is everything that surrounds an organism. It is by means of interaction with the environment that genetically conditioned dispositions develop.

It is also through the influence of the environment and the processes of adaptation that new forms arise. Adaptation favours certain genetic conditions in a certain period. With time, these dispositions spread in the population and remain until adaptation again demands change and favours other genes.

Learning may also be defined as a relationship between the individual and the environment. It is by registering the environmental responses to one's actions and by associating these with others that experience is built. Experience is learned knowledge.

The classic question of what influences behaviour most - inheritance or the environment—is still unanswered, and will probably remain that way. However, the question is out-dated. It is known that the environment can only act upon existing genetic disposition, and that genetic disposition can only develop into behaviour through specific environmental influence.

INHERITED BEHAVIOUR, EVOLUTION.

Escape

See **Flight.**

Ethology

Ethology (Greek, ethos = habit/fundamental characteristic and logia, logos = thought/reason/justification) is the science of behaviour. The methods of ethology differ from other sciences concerned with the study of behaviour in that ethology only uses explanations based on function and cause. Behaviour is explained in terms of how natural selection has shaped it and developed many variations. The ethological explanation is distinguished from the psychological which tries to explain behaviour from physiological processes or learning mechanisms. For the ethologist it is of vital importance to be able to study the animal in its natural environment.

THE HISTORY OF ETHOLOGY.

Ethology — The history of

Man's interest in animal behaviour is ancient and goes back to the very beginning of our history. Modern man, *Homo sapiens sapiens* became dominant about 30,000 years ago in the Upper Palaeolithic period. In the beginning of this period man produced great works of art, so called Ice Age art, or cave paintings, where pictures of animals predominate. The horse, the bison ox and the cow are the favourite animals in these drawings. These and other animals are drawn very accurately, which not only shows Homo sapiens sapiens' artistic ability, but also his knowledge of the animals. Hunting scenarios are also pictured. These are further clues which indicate that our ancestors possessed some significant knowledge about animals and animal behaviour.

The domestication of animals probably started about 11,500 years ago in the Middle East and in south west Asia. Domesticating animals, keeping them alive and breeding them must have demanded a certain amount of knowledge about their needs. The domestication of animals provided a constant source of meat, milk, eggs and so on. The Egyptians used animals for hunting purposes, as well as keeping them as pets. The first lexicon about animals was written by the Egyptians about 4,000 years BC. Dogs were very popular as pets in the Roman empire.

A certain school of Greek philosophy, the Cynics, which comes from 'kyon', the Greek word for dog, believed that animals were better than humans in many respects, for example in their lack of greed. They believed animals lacked reasoning, but had many other good qualities.

The first to study animal behaviour in a more scientific way by using precise observations without anthropomorphic comparisons was Aristotle, born in 384 BC. Aristotle didn't accept a radical distinction between biology and psychology. Two of Aristotle's ideas were especially important.

The first was *psuké,* which has many meanings, normally used as soul, but also encompassing life, the principle of life, life function. For instance, the concept was used to distinguish between different plants, animals and humans, all with different *psukhé*—life functions.

The other idea was nature's *ladder*, where Aristotle ordered animals and plants according to the complexity of their life forms. At the bottom there were inanimate things, then plants, then fungi, sea creatures, and so on, until we reached mammals and humans at the top. The difference between each rung was quantitative and that means humans had more of these characteristics than other animals. For example, they were better at reasoning than any other.

Galen (129-200 AD) concluded after several experiments that animals had inborn abilities such as certain behaviour patterns.

Al-Jahiz of Basra (767-868) wrote about experiments with animals which had been conducted with the purpose of describing their behaviour. He was concerned with communication in animals and with evolution.

Augustinus (354-430) and Thomas Aquinas (1224-1274) concluded that animals had feelings and that they should be treated kindly, for anyone who treated animals badly was likely to treat humans badly as well. Animals were of course different from humans, since they lacked souls.

A more scientific approach based on objective observations was used by Frederick the Second of Hohenstaufen (1194-1250) concerning the behaviour of birds, and by Albert Magnus (1200-1280) who studied the methodology of experimental observation. He introduced methods like repetition of experiments and the construction, confirmation, or denial of hypotheses.

Sir Thomas More (1478-1535) mentioned the importance of imprinting for the first time.

Pierre Belon (1517-1564) was one of the first observers of animal behaviour in the modern meaning of the word. He is regarded as the founder of comparative anatomy. His studies concentrated on birds and fish.

René Descartes (1596-1650) influenced our thoughts, up to the present day. His main hypothesis was that body and soul were two completely different things—dualism. He believed animals had no abstract reasoning or self-awareness, since these demanded the possession of a soul and animals had only mechanical, automatic bodily activity. Animals didn't have language, because the word was the sole sign of the presence of thought. His explanation was that all men, even the most stupid or foolish, made use of signs, whereas the brutes never did anything of the kind.

After Descartes followed the period where more and more scientists in England and on the Continent tried to explain behaviour and psychology from physiological or mechanical processes. The thoughts about the radical differences between humans and animals lost ground, especially thanks to John Locke, (1632-1704): 'There are some brutes that seem to have as much knowledge and reason as some that are called man...'

David Hume (1711-1776) wrote, 'Next to the ridicule of denying an evident truth, is that of taking such pains to defend it; and no truth appears to be more evident, than that beasts are endowed with thoughts and reasoning as well as men.'

Jean-Jacques Rousseau (1712-1778) wrote that humans and animals only differ in degrees of reason.

Charles George Leroy (1723-1789) was an ethologist in the modern sense of the word. His thoughts were based on accurate observations of animals in their natural environment. He argued against Descartes' philosophic observations. Man and animal were different, but animals surely act intelligently since the purpose of their actions fulfil their needs. Animals use memory and early experience. He states that for each species we should draw an ethogram containing information about the species, its way of life, habitat etc. Leroy describes, among others, the wolf and the fox's hunting behaviour.

Erasmus Darwin (1731-1802), Charles Darwin's grandfather, explained that some behaviour which had been considered instinctive could be a product of learning. He explained the evolution of the species by the adaptation of animals to their environment in order to survive.

Pierre-Jean Cabanis (1757-1809) looked at Darwin's thoughts in depth. He divided instincts into two classes: those dependant on structures developed before birth and those developed after birth.

Jean-Baptiste Lamarck (1744-1829) organised animals in groups based on the development of their nervous systems. His theory of evolution was based on his theory of behaviour. The animals acquired new behaviour patterns when the environment changed. The newly acquired behaviours were demanded by the animal's needs and were created by processes in the animal's nervous system. After continual repetition, these new behaviour patterns gradually became inherited and the species changed.

At the end of the 18th century, the word ethology began to appear. John Stuart Mill used it in 1843 as the science concerned with the study of character and the building of character. In 1859 Isidore Saint-Hillaire used the word ethology to describe research into the natural environment. Pierre Flourens in 1864 called the study of animals under laboratory conditions comparative psychology.

When W. M. Wheeler (1865-1937) and Oskar Heinroth (1871-1945) began using the word ethology it was already in the context of its modern meaning: the science studying animal behaviour in its natural environment.

In 1859 the most influential work was published: *The Origin of Species* by Charles Robert Darwin (1809-1882). Darwin was not only a keen observer with a constructive imagination, he was also an outstanding philosopher of science who was the first to structure thoughts and observations about animals, humans and life together in a scientific model.

His theory of evolution stated that animals which were especially adapted to a certain environment had greater chances to spread out their offspring, meaning that their characteristics would prevail in the population. If the environment changed, other individuals would then be better adapted to the new environment and would have better chances to influence the population with their genes. This was the way species developed and changed.

Darwin distinguished between instinct and intelligent behaviour, but didn't give us a clear definition of instinct. Complex instinctive action is the result of selection acting on simpler instincts.

In the *Expression of Emotions in Man and Animals* (1872), Darwin puts forward three principles of behaviour: (1) Behaviour assumes adequate forms for its purpose (the dog which is aggressive assumes positions which prepare it for attack); (2) The opposite behaviour is seen in the opposite case (the dog who is fearful, i.e., not aggressive, cowers); (3) Behaviour is influenced by the nervous system.

C Lloyd Morgan (1852-1936) contributed to the development of ethology in two main ways: first by being extremely critical in questions concerning methodology and thereafter by introducing and defining such ideas as reinforcement, inhibition, trial and error—concepts we still use today.

In the 20th century we have witnessed a rapid development in the study of behaviour. Opposing theories have been born and our knowledge, not only about animal behaviour, but also about our own behaviour has grown.

J. B. Watson (1878-1958) began by explaining behaviour as a physiochemical reaction to certain stimuli but later adhered to behaviourism. The behaviourists tried to explain behaviour uniquely from observational elements, as stimulus and response.

B. F. Skinner (1904-90) conducted many experiments with the purpose of clarifying the rules for conditioning. In 1903, in Madrid, Ivan P. Pavlov (1839-1946) published his studies about conditioned reflexes which had a great influence on Watson and Skinner's work.

Modern ethology was probably born with Oskar Heinroth (1871-1945). He published the *Ethology of the Anatidae* in 1910-11 where he recorded detailed studies of ducks and geese, their anatomy, social behaviour, communication patterns and their reproductive habits. Heinroth used comparative studies to describe behaviour as well as morphology and his ideas decisively influenced Lorenz and Tinbergen.

The work of Konrad Z. Lorenz (1903-1988) has been so significant, that it is impossible to describe here. His work has influenced all ethologists after him to such a degree that we can say modern ethology has two alternatives: either to confirm Lorenz's theories, or to prove them wrong, but there is no way to avoid his work.

Lorenz studied imprinting, the early and most decisive effects of environment which influence all young living beings. His theory of the instincts gave rise to some of the greatest discussions in the philosophy of science for ethology. Instincts are inherited and they develop independently of the environment. Instinctive behaviour is likely to be stereotypical for all members of the same species and is elicited by simple stimuli.

Daniel Lehrman among others, criticised Lorenz by saying that what an organism inherits can only be expressed in behaviour or something else through its relationship with the environment. Lorenz modified his theory: what the animal inherited is not an activity or a form of action, but a potential possibility for limited forms of behaviour where the genetic disposition is able to develop. Adaptation means that animals have information about the environment. This information is a result of natural selection through generations and the individual's acquired knowledge through experience. What the animal learns is thus dependant on the environment, as well as the animal's potential capacity for learning.

Nikolaas Tinbergen (1907-1988) worked with Lorenz on many projects. In 1951 he published his studies about instincts. In 1963 he produced the methodology of ethology as we know it today. He emphasised the importance of studying animals in their natural environment with the belief that only then can we conduct research to study such factors as motivation, development, survival value and evolution of various behaviour patterns.

Finally, in 1973, Konrad Lorenz, Nikolaas Tinbergen and Karl Von Frisch shared the Nobel prize in medicine—a great testimony to ethology as an independent science.

Evolution

Evolution means the development of an organism from earlier forms.

EVOLUTION THEORIES.

Evolution theories

Evolution theories explain how species, sub-species and variations originated.

Until the 19th century, several theories tried to explain species under the principle of divine creation. Animals behaved and appeared just as they were originally created—they didn't change radically and no new species had evolved. It was Charles Darwin in his *The Origin Of Species By Means Of Natural Selection* (1859) that first formulated the hypothesis that species evolved as a result of the struggle for life where the fittest always had an advantage. Darwin met much criticism. Today there is no scientist who would seriously defend the principle of the constancy of the species or the Bible's creation theory. However, as late as 1972 it was enforced by Californian law that school books mentioning Darwinism should also mention the Bible with equal weight.

It is very important to understand evolution in order to understand animal behaviour. Behaviour can only be explained and understood in evolutionary terms and as a tool for the main drives in the struggle for survival and reproduction. The fittest of all is the one able to stay alive as long as possible to increase its chances of successful reproduction so that its genetic information may be widespread in the universal genetic pool. Darwin's school of thought is so important that some authors are of the opinion that since 1859 and *The Origin of Species*, all biology and the biology of behaviour has been nothing else but a commentary on Darwin's book.

EVOLUTION, ETHOLOGY — THE HISTORY OF.

Exploration

Exploration is the behaviour shown by a dog when investigating objects or situations. Normally, the dog will move slowly, probably with a lowered head and ears flattened to the sides (unless the form of its ears prohibit this). New items are investigated at a distance, with characteristic sniffing movements where the dog tries to obtain as much olfactory information as possible—often by following a path along the wind direction. When the dog is close to the unidentified item, it tenses, ready to flee if necessary.

Caution is a necessity for all living organisms in order to survive. It is better to be watchful once too often than not. Prudence should not turn into fear, however, as this inhibits the dog's acquisition of knowledge.

CURIOSITY.

Extinction

Behaviour conditioned through reinforcement has to be maintained by presenting reinforcement on a regular basis or it will undergo extinction. A response is said to be extinguished when its rate has returned to its initial low level because responses have been emitted, but not followed by reinforcement.

REINFORCEMENT, REINFORCEMENT SCHEDULES, OPERANT CONDITIONING.

Eyebrow

When a dog is dominant its eyebrows usually appear very well-defined, while the submissive dog shows almost no eyebrows at all. Expressions of the eyebrows underline the expression of the eyes when showing both dominance and submission.

FACIAL EXPRESSIONS, EYES.

Eyes

The dominant and self-confident dog opens its eyes wide. As a dog becomes insecure and shows submissive behaviour the eyes become smaller and elongated. During pacifying displays, the eyes of the dog are small and narrowed. A dog engaged in extreme pacifying behaviour may even close its eyes.

Staring is the most common demonstration of dominance used by canids. Avoiding the stare of a dominant adversary is the most common pacifying gesture.

FACIAL EXPRESSIONS, GREETING, PACIFYING BEHAVIOUR, STARING, EYEBROW.

Face

Dogs' faces and heads come in many shapes and sizes. Variety has been achieved through mutation and selective breeding. Generally speaking, differences in markings and shapes emphasise communication signals, so that misunderstandings can be avoided. However, in some breeds we have twisted the proportions to such an extent that not only may communication difficulties arise, but physical suffering may also occur. Facial expressions are a major part of the dog's language.

FACIAL EXPRESSIONS, HEAD MARKINGS, EYES, EARS, LIPS, AGGRESSION, FEAR, LANGUAGE, DOMINANCE, SUBMISSION.

Different face types: Siberian Husky, Boxer and Pekinese.

Facial expressions

When we talk about facial expression, we refer to all the animal's expressions of the head, including the eyes and ears.

The wolf and the dog's facial expressions are identical. The only relevant differences are to be found in the variations of dog breeds where our selective breeding has produced anatomical differences, such as drooping ears, or a flat snout. In these dogs the same rules apply for those with wolf-like heads, but you need to be a keen observer to see their expressions.

Certain dog breeds adapt to these anatomical differences by exaggerating the expression of other body parts, as for example, dogs which wag their rear ends to compensate for their missing tails.

All facial expressions mirror a dog's motivation. The combination of these elements can emphasise or diminish other signals, giving the dog's facial expressions many variations.

HEAD MARKINGS, EYES, EARS, LIPS, FOREHEAD, SNOUT, AG-GRESSION, FEAR, DOMINANCE, SUBMISSION.

Expression	Motivation	Aggression	Dominance	Friendliness	Pacifying	Submission	Fear	Challenge	Threat
Eyes	big	x	x					x	x
	narrowed			x	x	x	x		
	averted gaze				x	x	x		
	staring	x	x					x	x
	blinking			x	x	x	x		
Ears	upright	x	x					x	x
	flattened			x	x	x			
	totally flattened					x	x		
	flickering				x	x	x		
Mouth	curled	x	x						
	drawn back			x	x	x			
Forehead	clear stop		x						
	flat					x			
Lips	raised	x							
	normal			x	x				
Muzzle	wrinkled	x							
	smooth			x	x				

See illustrations pages 110-113.

Canine facial expressions and body postures

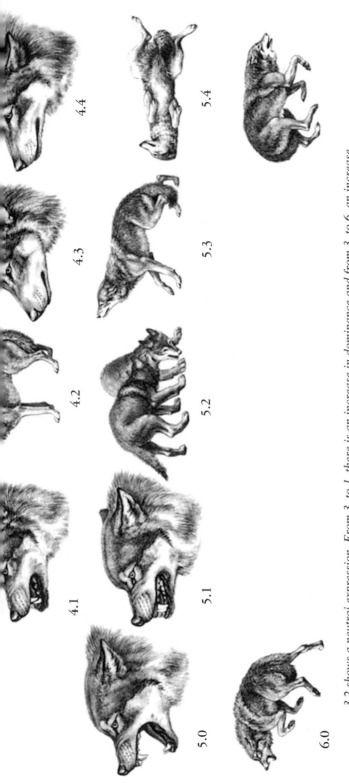

3.2 shows a neutral expression. From 3. to 1. there is an increase in dominance and from 3. to 6. an increase in submission. From .2 to .0 there is an increase in aggression and from .2 to .4 an increase in fear. Displays .2 show dominance and submission without aggression or fear.
Display 1.1. is the alpha wolf and 3.3. shows a greeting ceremony, a ritualised aggression and fear behaviour showing slight traces of dominance and submission.
Empty spaces, such as 2.0 and 3.0, have never been observed.

(*Dog Language* by Roger Abrantes , Wakan Tanka Publishers, 1997)

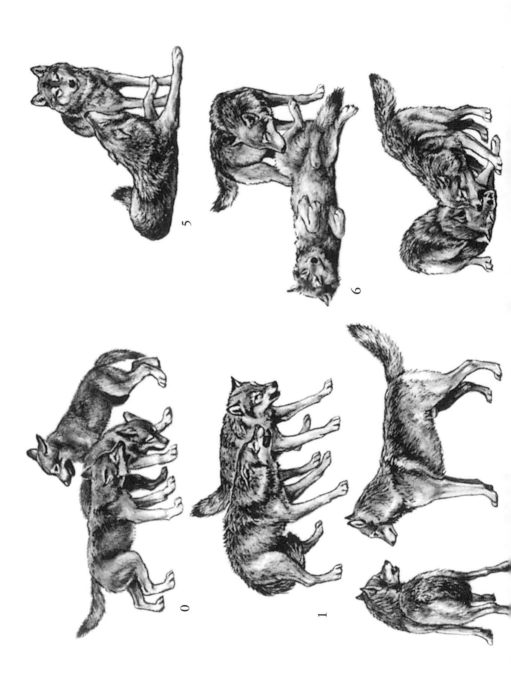

Canine facial expressi

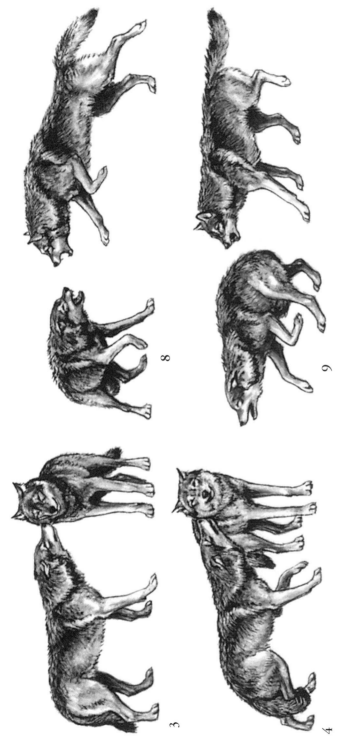

Dominance and submission have their own language. From 0 to 9 there is an increase of both dominance and submission. In 0 the cubs show that dominance and submission change constantly depending on specific circumstances. From 2 to 9 we see the submissive individual to the left and the dominant to the right. In 1, albeit showing submission and dominance, both wolves are more or less at the same level. In 2 the distance in rank is greater: the wolf to the right shows greater dominance, but pacifies its body by means of its ears and lips. In 3, 4 and partially in 5, the wolf to the left shows active submission and in 6 passive submission—its opponent is now clearly dominant. In 7 we see muzzle-grasp behaviour and an unequivocal accept of the opponents dominance. 8 shows a serious conflict—attack and defence (aggression and submission). 9 shows attack and flight (fear and submission).

(*Dog Language* by Roger Abrantes, Wakan Tanka Publishers 1997)

body postures

Faeces

See **Defecation.**

False pregnancy

When female dogs behave as if they were pregnant or had just given birth, we say they are suffering from false or phantom pregnancy. The female will usually dig to build a nest site and she may take socks, shoes, balls, bones or other objects to the den and watch them as carefully as if they were puppies. False pregnancy is caused by hormonal changes. It is not unusual for a female to behave as if she was pregnant for a period of about two months after her season. This is a very significant behaviour for wolves, as it ensures that females are more motivated to accept the oncoming cubs, protect them, take care of them and show the whole range of necessary maternal behaviour.

Behaviour during false pregnancy is very interesting. It is an example of normal and purposeful behaviour in the wild which has lost its function and is now a nuisance for owners of domesticated dogs.

Occasionally, the behaviour of the female suffering from the false pregnancy is so aggravated it causes the threshold for aggressive behaviour to become much lower. Dog owners should be careful when approaching females suffering from false pregnancy. The dog is likely to show aggression, or even bite, if the owner tries to remove objects from the nest site. Special care should also be taken when receiving visitors accompanied by dogs. In these cases, dog owners are recommended to contact their veterinary surgeon for hormonal treatment for their pet or advice regarding prevention of future false pregnancies.

In milder cases, encouraging the dog to be more active may help. This will not solve the problem directly, but may alleviate symptoms by giving the dog other activities on which to concentrate.

HORMONES, MATERNAL BEHAVIOUR.

Fear

Fear is the motivational factor which elicits flight or defence. Fear is a stress situation where the individual's apprehension of certain situations triggers a series of physiological and anatomical processes in order to deal with the situation in the best possible way. Considered to be motivation, fear, like aggression, is one of the major mechanisms involving huge physiological and psychological resources.

Fear can cause pathological behaviour when the individual is exposed to fear-eliciting stimuli for too long. Fear is always connected to submission. If the submissive individual becomes self-assured then submission will give way to dominance and fear disappears.

There are two types of fear: existential and social. Existential fear deals with self-preservation. Theoretically, there are two strategies available: flight or fight, but in practice, flight is often the only available option. Unlike social fear, situations eliciting existential fear do not allow any possibility of compromise, such as submission. When a cat chases a mouse the only strategy for the mouse is to flee. Much of the existential fear is elicited by external stimuli which can be recognised without previous learning or experience. The ability to recognise these stimuli is genetically programmed in the individual. For example, wolf cubs run into their den when they hear certain acoustic signals from adult pack members.

Social fear is elicited by conflicts with other members of the same species. Fight and flight are still two available strategies, but in these cases there is a possibility of compromise. Submission is a compromise. Social fear is often elicited by previously learned stimuli. If a dog has unpleasant experiences several times in a certain location, the location itself will elicit fear. An unpleasant experience with certain people may also be enough to elicit fear by the mere sight of them. Dog owners need to be careful to avoid reinforcing the fear in their puppies with their own behaviour. For example, during a visit to the vets, owners should be very much aware of their own behaviour and how it influences the puppy. On many occasions, owners with good intentions try to comfort their puppies, but unfortunately they are actually reinforcing the puppy's fear of the place. The training class, the dog's resting place and so on, should also be unconnected with fear.

Facial and body expressions express fear. The wolves in the upper row show fear—small eyes, retracted lips, flat forehead, ears laid back. At the bottom left we see active submission, in the middle passive submission and to the right flight behaviour. Fear and submission occur simultaneously.

All wolves in the illustration show submission—greatest however in the bottom row.

The interaction between fear, aggression, dominance and submission results in the various expressions used by the dog in social interaction. They give rise to what we call *dog language* . The dog's expression of the conflicts between these motivating factors is very detailed. Through the various behaviour patterns, dogs are able to inform each other very accurately of their intentions and desires. This is very important for social animals and enables dogs living in packs to avoid serious confrontations which could result in life-threatening damage. People may also avoid confrontations if they can read dogs' expressions.

In conflict situations between members of the same species, fear will normally cause pacifying behaviour where the fearful individual tries to inform the threatening dog that it accepts its demands, through active submission. If fear and submission in a specific situation increases, the fearful and submissive individual will show passive submission. If this does not have the desired effect—pacifying the opponent and ending the conflict—it will flee.

If flight is impossible then active defence will take place through behaviour which clearly shows the conflict between submission and aggression. Fear is then supplanted by aggression, when passive and active submission and flight are ineffective, although submission is still detected in the animal's behaviour. The dog is then fearful and submissive and not fearful and aggressive as popular opinion often states.

The level and degree of fear can vary greatly and this can be clearly observed in the dog's facial expression and body language.

AGGRESSION, PHOBIA, MOTIVATION, STRESS, PACIFYING BE-HAVIOUR, ACTIVE SUBMISSION, STIMULUS, CONDITIONED BE-HAVIOUR, OPERANT CONDITIONING, INBORN BEHAVIOUR, IN-HERITED BEHAVIOUR, DOMINANCE, SUBMISSION.

Fear of enclosed spaces

See **Claustrophobia.**

Fear of open spaces

See **Agoraphobia.**

Fear of strangers

See **Xenophobia.**

Fighting

Fighting comprises all forms of conflict behaviour between at least two dogs. It is rare that animals fight with members of another species, although this can happen in situations over killed prey. In these exceptional cases, we may explain the animals' behaviour as being motivated by aggression. Predators do not fight with the prey, since the hunt is not motivated by aggression, but by self-preservation and hunger.

During fighting, we may observe all a dog's behaviour traits—aggression, fear, dominance, submission and flight. Wolves usually solve their conflicts through threats, symbolic attack and flight. It is rare that two wolves hurt each other seriously during a fight. Normally, conflicts are preceded by very clear warnings so that both contenders are well prepared. An exception to this rule is seen when two wolves initiate the final contest after many previous minor fights. This happens without warning and is uninhibited. They then fight to kill, or to force the other to leave the pack, not to obtain dominance.

Our dogs show the same fighting behaviour as wolves. However, our selection of stock has lowered the threshold for the display of peaceful or symbolic attack/flight behaviour. Also, some of our dogs do not show the same degree of inhibition when necessary.

AGGRESSION, FEAR, DOMINANCE, SUBMISSION, AGONISTIC BEHAVIOUR, INHIBITIONS.

Fitness

Fitness is the animal's ability to deal with certain circumstances and environmental changes. This concept is central to the theory of evolution. Darwin speaks of the *survival of the fittest*. The fittest doesn't necessarily need to be the strongest, but is generally the one who best exploits the available resources at a certain time, such as terrain, food, presence of conspecifics and so on. It is always the fittest which has the greatest chance of surviving long enough to find a partner, mate and have offspring which will inherit its characteristics. After some generations, the characteristics of the fittest will be most prevalent in that habitat. The idea of the fittest is not a static concept. The fittest at a certain time and under certain circumstances in a population is not necessarily the fittest under different circumstances at another time.

When man domesticated the dog he made the natural mechanism of selection redundant. The fittest dog became a decision based on his criteria for beauty and usefulness. Occasionally, we observe pathological behaviour in our dogs which is a direct product of selection. In natural conditions these individuals would die and the genetic information causing the pathological behaviour would disappear. These individuals wouldn't influence the population they belong to. However, we choose to breed from these animals. For example, dogs lacking parental abilities, those that show extreme aggression, fear, or who lack the ability to show social behaviour would most probably disappear in a world of natural selection. Kennel clubs throughout the world should think carefully about this and revise their criterion of breeds according to a sound long-term strategy.

In social animals the concept of fitness is very important to the development of social behaviour, and especially the development of communication patterns. The fittest social animal is not normally the most aggressive or the most peaceful, but is the one that uses these traits to best advantage.

SURVIVAL, EVOLUTION THEORIES.

Flehmen

Flehmen (German) is the act of drawing olfactory information through the Jacobson's organ.

JACOBSON'S ORGAN, SCENT, SCENT SIGNALS.

Flight

Flight is a stress reaction elicited by danger, or fear. Flight behaviour is mostly instinctive. Puppies show flight behaviour when their mother barks or snarls in a specific way. A healthy flight mechanism is absolutely vital for all animals to survive. It is often better to choose flight rather than fight. When flight is elicited by conflict between members of the same species, the fleeing animal shows submission and fear. The dog crouches, covers its genitals with its tail, draws back its lips, makes its eyes appear small and flattens its ears.

Fligth is a stress reaction vital for survival.

Prey animals have better developed and specialised flight behaviour patterns than predators, such as using evasive manoeuvres and behaviour aimed at confusing the predator. Some show protean behaviour (from the Greek hero Proteus, who, according to the legend escaped from his enemies by assuming various forms). For instance, they may make unpredictable changes in direction, or they manage to directly deceive predators - such as the moth which responds to a bat's echo location by sending false signals.

FEAR, SUBMISSION, STRESS.

Forehead

The dog's forehead reflects dominance and submission, or superiority and inferiority. If the forehead, or rather the skin on the forehead, is smooth and tight, it shows submission. If, on the other hand, the stop is well-defined, it could mean that the dog is showing dominance, but to be sure of this other body signals must be observed.

The expressions of the forehead should only be taken as supplementary in defining the motivation of the dog. The expressions of the ears, eyes and lips should always be taken into account as well.

FACIAL EXPRESSIONS, EYES, EARS, LIPS.

If the forehead, or rather the skin on the forehead, is smooth and tight, it shows submission or friendliness as in above illustration.

Friendliness

See **Pacifying behaviour** and **Greeting**.

Gait

See **Movement.**

Gene

See **DNA and Genetics.**

Genetics

Genetics (Greek, genesis = origin/creation) is the science of inheritance.

INHERITED BEHAVIOUR.

Genital sniffing

Sniffing another dog's genitals provides a dog with valuable information. It is a form of identification. The male dog's sexual behaviour is elicited by the female's oestrus and sniffing is always seen as a preliminary to courtship behaviour.

Dogs also sniff each other's genitals as a normal greeting behaviour. Females which are not in oestrus may object to intense sniffing from males. Puppies or very submissive dogs may produce a few drops of urine to underline their submission.

Some dog owners think it is disgusting when their dogs engage in genital sniffing procedures with strange dogs they meet, yet this is a perfectly natural way for dogs to interact.

GENITALS, OESTRUS, GREETING, SCENT, SEXUAL BEHAVIOUR, COURTSHIP BEHAVIOUR, SEXUAL ORGANS.

Sniffing another dog's genitals provides a dog with information. Dogs also sniff each other's genitals as a normal greeting behaviour.

Genitals

Genitals, or genitalia, (Latin, genitalia, from genus = birth/race/stock) are the external organs of reproduction. Some dog behaviour is associated with the genitals, like mutual sniffing during the first phase of greeting ceremonies.

SEXUAL ORGANS, GREETING, MATING.

Genotype

Genotype (Greek, genotypus, génos = race and typus or tupos = impression/figure) is the genetic constitution of an individual, in contrast to the phenotype, which is the external appearance of an individual. Unlike the phenotype, the genotype is not visible.

PHENOTYPE, GENETICS.

Greeting

Greeting is the behaviour seen when two individuals of the same species meet and assure each other of peaceful intentions. Greeting behaviour is an offshoot of aggression—it is ritualised behaviour. When two aggressive animals meet, instead of killing each other, they engage in greeting rituals. Greeting ceremonies comprise of many other modified behaviours, such as sexual and parental behaviour. Greeting ceremonies are very important for all social animals as they are genetically programmed to regard strangers with suspicion. This is also the reason why strangers always actively engage in these greeting ceremonies.

When two dogs greet each other, they start by carefully sniffing at each others' muzzles and then go on to sniff each other's genitals. After this first approach they can then go on to play if they are more or less equal in age and rank, or they will display their respective rank to each other. In this case, the submissive dog will normally be the most active of the two and it will be very eager to show active submission. It will flatten its ears, draw back its lips, make its eyes appear small and so on, and it will use a muzzle-nudge or lick the other around the lips. The dominant dog shows friendliness by closing its eyes a little, drawing its ears back slightly and by turning its head away, to expose the side of its throat. If the difference between their ranks is even greater, the submissive individual will display passive submission by lying down on its back and inviting the dominant one to sniff its genitals. If the submissive dog is fearful, it may produce a few drops of urine to emphasise that it is totally submissive. The submissive one appeals to the other's sense of parental care by acting as if it was a puppy.

When humans meet dogs we should always give them sufficient time to engage in greeting ceremonies. We should not walk towards the dog with an outstretched hand, as we do when we greet each other. We should crouch down, turn our heads away from the dog and avoid staring at it. Our behaviour then shows self-assurance and friendliness and it is entirely up to the dog to make the next move. Most dogs then greet us in a friendly way. However, some care should be taken, since unfortunately there are dogs who do not seem to recognise friendly behaviour either in humans or other dogs and may attack without warning or inhibition.

Many problems between dogs and people in training classes are caused by a

When two wolves meet they greet one another showing ritualized behaviour. The wolf to the right shows submissive and pacifying behaviour—muzzle nudge. The wolf to the left shows dominance and acceptance of the lower ranking individual—it turns its head away with laid back ears, half closed eyes and retracted lips.

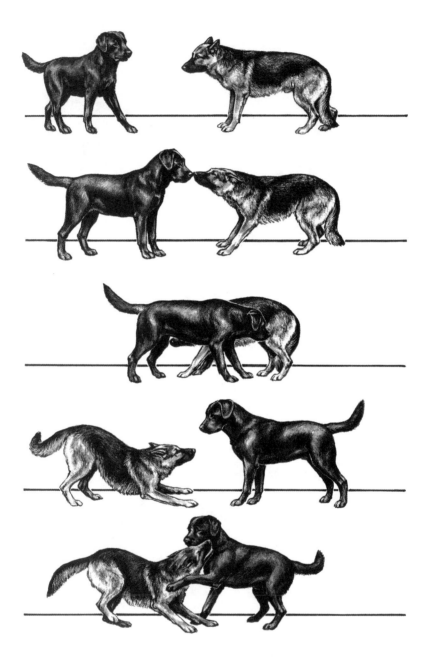

When two dogs greet each other, they start by carefully sniffing at each others'
muzzles and then go on to sniff each other's genitals. After this first approach they
can then go on to play if they are more or less equal in age and rank, or they will
display their respective rank to each other.

lack of recognition of the importance of greeting rituals. All trainers and instructors should tell their classes about the importance and the range of behavioural traits of the dog in greeting and they should sacrifice at least the first ten or fifteen minutes of the class to make sure that all dogs and humans are well acquainted with each other according to each species' specific needs.

AGGRESSION, FEAR, RITUALS, FRIENDLINESS, PEOPLE AND DOGS.

Grooming

Grooming behaviour is related to hygiene. However, the dog's grooming behaviour is not highly developed. Originally, grooming was probably not necessary, since the dog's ancestor, the wolf, has a self-cleaning coat which does not need special care. It moults during summer and grows during win-

Dogs do sometimes groom each other, but this is rare and only occurs between animals who know each other very well.

ter. The wolf's coat protects it against heat and cold and acts as a buffer against strong wind and rain. If the animal is healthy, its coat is not a source of problems.

In our domestic dogs the coat may often be problematic. Some breeds have coats which are very resistant to all weather conditions, while others provide no protection at all, but only serve to satisfy our sense of beauty.

Dogs often lick their paws and legs and clean their genitals. They catch fleas with difficulty since an undershot, overshot or scissor bite is much less effective than a level bite in locating parasites.

Dogs do sometimes groom each other, but this is rare and only occurs between animals who know each other very well. Mothers routinely groom their puppies. Males may lick females in heat but this is obviously motivated by factors other than grooming or parental care. Otherwise, it is common to see dogs licking other dogs' eyes or the region around the eyes and ears. This kind of licking sometimes becomes compulsive, which raises questions about the true motivation of this behaviour.

Group

See **Pack.**

Growl

A growl is a deep threatening sound. A growl is an aggressive act, similar to our own 'enough is enough'!

AGGRESSION, MOTIVATION, SNARL, COMMUNICATION.

Guilt

See **Conscience.**

Golden Retrievers and Cocker Spaniels are very popular gun dogs as well as family dogs.

Gundogs

Gundogs were originally bred to fulfil our hunting needs. Gundogs are specialists in particular forms of hunting, but a gundog will still have all the general abilities and needs that members of the genus family *Canis familiaris* have.

Dog owners should not be concerned that they do not go hunting if they have gundogs as pets. As long as the dog is given the opportunity of developing its abilities and satisfying its needs it will be well-balanced and content.

PREDATORY BEHAVIOUR.

Habit

Habits are behaviour patterns which are frequently displayed. The advantage of habits is that the individual does not need to use a great amount of energy in order to produce the behaviour pattern in question. Habits save energy in as much as they do not require great brain activity and feed-back from the senses.

All animals develop habits and our dogs are very likely to perform the same routines day after day. We should encourage our dogs to build habits which benefit our own daily routine, such as a walk to the park or round the block two or three times a day.

Habits are easily built, only necessitating a few repetitions. However, they are difficult to break and sometimes sophisticated processes are needed to do so.

Habitat

A habitat is the organism's environment, which contains all the factors that it needs to survive and develop normal behaviour patterns. It is important to understand an animal's habitat in order to fully grasp its behaviour. According to certain theories it is a species' habitat which gives it its typical behaviour.

BEHAVIOUR THEORIES, ECOLOGY.

Hackles

Hackles are hairs on the dog's back which are raised in a situation where the dog is taken by surprise. Some dogs raise all the hairs from the neck to the root of the tail, others only the hairs near the neck, while others raise the hairs near the neck and near the root of the tail, giving them a very peculiar appearance. Raising the hackles is a psychosomatic reaction. It is the dog's perception of the situation which causes the physiological and anatomical reaction of raised hackles.

Raised hackles are often seen as an indication of aggression. This is due to the fact that the dog normally assumes positions where it tries to appear big and imposing when aggressive. However, raising the hackles normally appears when the dog is taken by surprise and shows submission. In normal conditions, the dominant and self-assured dog does not need to raise its hackles since all its body attitudes show strength. The fearful, submissive and surprised dog probably raises its hackles to frighten its opponent. If it succeeds in making its opponent hesitate for a moment it will have a better chance to prepare its defence, or flee.

FEAR.

Raised hackles are often seen as an indication of aggression. However, raising the hackles normally appears when the dog is taken by surprise and shows submission.

Head markings seem to emphasise facial expressions. This leads to the assumption that markings enhance those elements in the dog's face that are relevant to communication.

Head markings

Head markings arise from different coat patterns on the dog's head and face. In nature, regularities seldom arise without long-term benefits to survival. It is therefore tempting to look at head markings from this point of view. All markings seem to emphasise facial expressions, and clear markings are usually seen in animals with highly developed communication systems; social animals. This leads to the assumption that markings enhance those elements in the dog's face that are relevant to communication.

Head markings in the dog arose from mutations in the wolf. In the Grey Wolf we see similar patterns or markings, although they are usually less obvious than in domestic dog breeds. Very obvious markings, such as the Siberian Husky's, may allow clearer communication, while a black-coloured coat may contribute to misunderstandings between individuals. However, there is no satisfactory research leading to this conclusion.

FACIAL EXPRESSIONS, AGGRESSION, FEAR, FACE, COMMUNICATION.

Hearing

The dog's hearing is much better developed than the human's. The dog is able to register sounds at a greater distance and locate them much more accurately.

Dog owners should consider this fact when they shout at their dogs, and trainers should bear this in mind if they inform their pupils that shouting is the only way to make the dog know who is in charge. This is certainly not

Attentive dogs direct their ears towards the source of sound.

true. Shouting doesn't solve any problems and may even worsen them. A confused dog will not understand us any better if we shout at it and shouting certainly doesn't make dogs more motivated. It is very important for all dog owners to know exactly how their dogs perceive their world and the signals we give them. Effective learning depends on the accurate use of appropriate learning methods as well as knowledge of the pupil's perceptive abilities.

EARS, SENSE ORGANS, COMMUNICATION, PEOPLE AND DOGS.

Heat

Heat, or season, is the period where the female undergoes physiological processes which trigger her sexual behaviour, and the male's sexual behaviour in turn.

The wolf comes into season once a year, usually in February or March. The domestic dog normally comes into season twice a year, but it is not abnormal or a sign of ill health if they only come into season once a year.

SEXUAL BEHAVIOUR, OESTRUS.

Hereditary behaviour

See **Inherited behaviour.**

Hip nudge

A hip nudge is the behaviour shown when the dog nudges another with its hip or rear end. Dogs often use this sort of behaviour towards people, typically during greeting ceremonies when we show the dog passive friendliness by crouching down to it. The dog will then walk towards us, turn round and either nudge gently with the hip or rear end, or stand passively with its back turned to us. The hip nudge means friendliness. By turning its back to

Dogs often use this sort of behaviour towards people, typically during greeting ceremonies. A hip nudge means friendliness.

us the dog shows that it doesn't intend to attack —it turns its teeth away. At the same time it shows that it trusts us.

The same behavioural pattern, although modified, is used during mating rituals where the male nudges the female.

GREETING, PACIFYING BEHAVIOUR.

Hormones

Hormones (Greek, hormón, horman, hormé = impulse/impel/to urge on) are substances primarily formed by the endocrine glands that pass to the blood or sap and stimulate various organs. The function of the hormones are to regulate physiological processes. Some of these physiological processes have a more direct connection with behaviour than others. For example, the female's season (oestrus) is a hormonal process which compels the female to show sexual behaviour. However, hormones cannot be said to compel the animal to act in a certain way. Instead, they provide the right physiological background for a certain behaviour to be displayed if and when other necessary conditions, ie early experience, environment and eliciting stimuli, occur.

There are three ways that hormones operate: 1) By influencing certain parts of the organism necessary for the performance of a specific behaviour, 2) By changing the threshold values in the sensory systems, thereby altering the function of the brain, 3) By directly influencing the brain. These factors are not mutually exclusive.

Glandotrophic hormones are formed in the anterior lobe of the pituitary gland and have a stimulating effect on glands. The *gonadotrophic hormones* stimulate the sexual glands: *follicle stimulating hormone* (FSH) influences the production of sperm cells in males and in females influences the development of the Graafian follicle in the ovary, stimulating the ovary to secrete *oestrogen. Luteinising hormone* (LH) stimulates ovulation in females and changes the Graafian follicle into the *corpus luteum* ('yellow body') and in males, increases the production of *androgens* in the testicles. *Thyreothrophin* stimulates the thyroid gland, while *adreno-cortico-trophic hormone* (ACTH) from the anterior lobe of the pituitary gland stimulates production of *adrenalin* in the adrenal cortex and *prolactin* stimulates milk production.

In the anterior lobe of the pituitary gland the growth hormone responsible for rate of growth is also produced.

Oxytocin is produced by the posterior lobe of the pituitary gland and is responsible for the contractions of the uterus during parturition (birth) and the production of milk.

Thyroxin, which is produced in the thyroid gland (*thyroidea*), influences the metabolism and the regulation of temperature.

Insulin is produced in the pancreas. Its function is to regulate blood sugar. The *adrenal cortical hormones*, such as *cortisole, cortisone* and *corticosterone* are produced by the *adrenal cortex* and have many functions, such as the regulation of metabolic functions, namely the body's utilisation of glucose and the maintenance of salt levels.

Adrenaline and noradrenaline are secreted by the adrenal glands and are often called stress hormones because they prepare the body for action in emergencies, increasing heart rate, blood pressure and blood sugar.

Androgens are the male sexual hormones: androsterone and testosterone. They are produced in the testicles and cause the development of sexual organs and sexual behaviour.

Oestrogens are produced in the follicles of the ovary and are female sexual hormones. They influence the female's sexual organs' development and sexual behaviour. Oestrogens are also registered in the male's urine, while androsterones are registered in the female's.

Progesterone is secreted in the ovaries and regulates oestrus and pregnancy.

PHYSIOLOGY, PHEROMONE, SEXUAL BEHAVIOUR, OESTRUS.

Howl

The characteristic wolf howl is one of the communication patterns that our dogs have inherited. Normally, wolves howl in sequences of up to 20 seconds.

The purpose of the howl seems to be: 1) To give information about territorial boundaries to neighbouring packs, 2) To strengthen the bond between pack members, 3) To enable a lone wolf to locate and establish contact with other lone wolves.

A low-ranking wolf is less likely to trigger the pack to howl than a high-ranking member. Higher-ranking individuals are particularly prone to howling if they cannot find their partners, other high-ranking wolves, or cubs. The pack is more likely to howl if separated from a high-ranking wolf than from a low-ranking one. A wolf howls in many different ways, depending on whether it is starting the howling chorus or is responding to it. There are individual characteristics in the way wolves howl—each wolf is known by its own howl. It is possible that by howling wolves are giving each other more detailed information than we are presently able to perceive. European wolves and American wolves howl differently— could this be a difference of dialect?!

Our dogs howl just like the wolf, but without the same meaning. Dogs howl when they are lonely, but seldom to strengthen the bonds of the pack, and never for territorial reasons. The howl is contagious. If one dog begins howling it will probably trigger the howling of two or three other dogs in the neighbourhood. If we try to imitate the howling the chances are we will be accompanied by our dogs. Sirens from police cars, ambulances, fire engines and so on are also likely to trigger howling. Some owners also complain that their dogs howl when they play the piano, although this may be a reflection of their musical abilities!

RITUALS, ALLELOMIMETIC BEHAVIOUR.

Humanising

See **Anthropomorphism.**

Hunger

Hunger is the stimulation of physiological processes which lead the animal to find food. Predators hunt when they are hungry.

Hunger may influence the social order of a pack, in as much as it increases the readiness of the animal to react to others. Animals are generally more aggressive when hungry, since they are ready to fight for food. The ability to find food, serving the drive of self-preservation, may be a selective factor. The individuals which are best at finding food have the greatest chances of survival and of providing food for their progeny—they are the fittest.

Hunger is a very strong motivational factor and it can be used in artificial learning situations with great success. Titbits can be used to condition certain behaviour patterns, or as reinforcers.

DRIVE, SELF-PRESERVATION, SELECTION.

Hunting

See **Predatory behaviour.**

Hyperactivity

Dogs which show a greater level of activity than the average in the breed and population are commonly called hyperactive.

There are several reasons for hyperactivity which can be traced back to physiological processes. Owners of dogs showing a greater level of activity than expected are therefore advised to contact their veterinary surgeon in order to have the dog thoroughly checked and eventually treated. Allergy or diet may also be the cause or a contributory factor to displays of hyperactivity. After consulting the veterinary surgeon, the owner should also contact a recognised behaviourist or behaviour therapist for help in implementing a supplementary behaviour programme.

Hyperactivity is often the result of under-stimulation. When the dog does not use its abilities or satisfies its needs sufficiently, it is likely to over-react at the first possible occasion.

UNDER-STIMULATION.

Imitation

A behaviour is said to be imitated when an animal deliberately does the same as another after having observed it. Observation and deliberation are essential elements of true imitation.

There are many examples of imitated behaviour in the animal kingdom. However, it is difficult to distinguish imitated behaviour from allelomimetic behaviour in dogs. When a dog digs a hole and another begins digging as well, it is probable that the second dog is simply motivated to find out what smells interesting. The second dog would probably have dug in the same place as well, if it had got there first.

The concept of imitation has an historical interest, as Darwin used it to prove that *mind* could be found in varying degrees in many animals. The ability of animals to imitate was taken as evidence supporting the idea that *mind* was involved.

ALLELOMIMETIC BEHAVIOUR.

Imprinting

Imprinting is the influence of the environment on all living beings immediately after birth and thereafter. At this time, animals are imprinted to environmental stimuli which they will use later in life to judge situations and take decisions. They are imprinted to conspecifics, food and everything which subsequently plays an important role in their struggle for survival.

If puppies are not imprinted to humans before they reach seven weeks old, they will never consider humans as social partners. We may be able to tame them, in the same way we tame wild animals, but the human-dog bond which is so characteristic of the owner-dog relationship will not be present. These dogs cannot be integrated into human society as pets. Research shows that a few minutes of body contact with humans every day during the first couple of weeks of their lives may be enough to imprint wolf cubs to humans. Without this body contact they would remain fearful and distant.

Imprinting is irreversible—it can not be deleted or changed after it has taken place. The effect of specific imprinting towards certain items such as food, may however be reduced.

LEARNING THEORIES, ENVIRONMENT.

Inborn behaviour

Inborn behaviour is everything which is not acquired by learning. A puppy's inborn behaviour includes the ability to find warmth, teats and to be able to suckle.

Dogs show less inborn behaviour than is popularly assumed. There are many apparently inborn elements which require specific environmental conditions in order to develop into behavioural traits which are common to 'higher' animals.

INHERITED BEHAVIOUR.

Infantile behaviour

Infantile (from infant, Latin, in fans/fantis, part of fari = to speak. Infantis = unable to speak) behaviour is the behaviour shown by young individuals. Some infantile behaviour is later modified and included in the dog's normal social communication patterns.

Examples of infantile behaviour in dogs (see next page).

Behaviour	Origin	Later meaning
Suckling movements	Lactating	Lip-smacking = pacifying
Teat-nudge	Seeking for the teats	Muzzle-nudge = pacifying
Lifting the hind leg	Forced by the mother's wish to lick belly and genitals Lying on the back	Twist movement = pacifying = passive submission
Kneading movements	Stimulates milk production	Paw lifting = submissive friendliness Pawing 1 = active submission Pawing 2 = attention-seeking
Lip licking and nudge	To elicit regurgitating	Muzzle-nudge = pacifying behaviour from adults
Eye closing	In connection with maternal	Narrowed eyes = friendliness, attention Blink = submission or fear
Play-face	Invitation to play	Play-face = pacifying
Play-bow	Invitation to play of courtship behaviour	Play-bow = pacifying or part

Infantile behaviour is of vital importance for the puppy and it is therefore inborn. Many of the patterns are seen in a rudimentary form just after birth, although puppies get better at these patterns as their motor skills improve. The puppy's muzzle-nudge on the mother's teats later assumes the meaning of friendliness. The mother's licking of the puppy's belly and genitals, forcing the puppy to lift one hind leg, is later modified into the twist movement which is a pacifying gesture.

LIP-SMACKING, MUZZLE-NUDGE, TWIST MOVEMENT, KNEA-DING, PAWING, BLINKING, EYES, PLAY-FACE, PLAY-BOW.

Infantile behaviour is mainly due to the transition to solid food. Pups lick each other and they try to force adults to regurgitate food to them by licking their lips frenetically. These behaviour forms will later assume the function to pacify an opponent. Dogs also use muzzle nudge behaviour towards humans to show their friendliness and accept of our dominant role.

Inferiority

Inferiority means being lower in position, degree, rank or merit. There is also a psychological use of this concept as 'inferiority complex'. In ethological terms, inferiority means the behaviour of a lower-ranking member of a pack. Inferior behaviour is submissive behaviour. Sometimes this behaviour can also be described by using the term insecurity. In all cases, the behavioural display is the same.

SUBMISSION.

Information

Information is a difference that makes the difference. Information is always informative and is not simply a vague concept. Something which is not perceived directly may dramatically alter another's behaviour. For example, information may have no meaning for one person, yet gives vital information to another. When communicating with our dogs we must bear in mind that they do not put the same value on some aspects of communication as we do. It is therefore advantageous to try to 'think dog'.

Inherited behaviour

Inherited, or genetically conditioned behaviour can only be applied to very simple behaviour traits which are performed stereotypically by all members of the same species. For example, instinctive behaviour is inherited behaviour, since the same stimuli elicits the same behaviour in all individuals.

All behaviour is genetically conditioned, since no behavioural trait can develop without a genetic disposition for it. On the other hand, there are few genetic dispositions which would develop into behaviour without a suitable environment. Behaviour is thus the result of the animals' genetic disposition when or after it has been influenced by the environment. We may inhibit or promote certain traits in an animal by means of the appropriate or inappropriate environment for the development of that specific trait.

It is therefore impossible to say there are certain genes for certain behaviours, but rather there are certain genes which allow for the development of specific behaviour under specific conditions. All behaviour is genetically quantitative. No dog possesses only aggressive genes and no dog possesses only peaceful ones. All dogs have all sorts of genes, only in different degrees. The aggressive dog, in contrast to the peaceful one, has genes which programme it to respond more quickly, or more violently, in certain circumstances. The peaceful dog also has a certain amount of the same genes which programme it to show aggression, but it will need more input from a certain circumstance to show aggression—aggression is triggered at a higher threshold.

Some forms of behaviour require many environmental stimuli before the genetic disposition is revealed. Others require very few. When we say that a dog is aggressive and it is inherited, we mean that under the influence of every environment it would develop aggressive behaviour. Only in this way is it meaningful to talk of inherited or non-inherited behaviour. However, we must bear in mind that all behaviour is the product of interaction between genes and the environment.

GENETICS.

Inhibitions

Inhibitions are the mechanisms which compel an animal to interrupt an action in the middle of a sequence. For example, when two wolves fight and one lies on its back with its belly up and its throat exposed, the opponent limits itself to snarling close to the other's belly and throat, without biting. Inhibition mechanisms play a major role in contact between aggressive social animals due to the fact that they prevent damage and death as a consequence of conflict. Inhibition mechanisms are very powerful, as they have life-saving effects. For instance, healthy dogs show a very distinctive bite inhibition mechanism. If conflicts cannot be solved by displays of dominance and submission, they may fight. Sometimes these fights are very vigorous and yet when it is over, no damage has been done to either dog. Inhibition mechanisms are switched off during conflicts when a dog wants to get rid of the opponent, but never to settle mere rank ordering disputes. Wolves only show uninhibited attacks when they want to force an opponent to leave the pack, as for instance, when the alpha female is in heat and finds herself in direct conflict with competitors.

Most inhibition mechanisms arise from parental instinct and the inborn recognition of infantile behaviour. Wolves and dogs inhibit their opponent by appealing to their parental instincts. Wolves and dogs that lie down with belly and throat exposed are as vulnerable as a puppy.

The characteristic 'twist' movements that puppies display with one hind leg turned out, when trying to pacify an adult opponent, remind the attacking individual of the helplessness of the puppy.

In principle, our dogs show all the inhibition mechanisms that selection found purposeful for their ancestor, the wolf. However, our selective breeding from specific individuals has weakened the demonstration of these behavioural traits in certain groups and many of our dog breeds show a disturbing lack of inhibition. This has most dangerous implications for such an aggressive social animal as the dog. Breeders should therefore be very careful when choosing their breeding stock and never breed from dogs showing uninhibited behaviour or dogs from families showing this type of behaviour.

PARENTAL CARE, INFANTILE BEHAVIOUR, TWIST MOVEMENT, FIGHTING, BITE INHIBITION.

Instinct

Instinct (Latin, instinctus, stinguere = incite) is the inborn ability to perform a complete action or a sequence of actions. For example, puppies know how to find their mother's nipples and suckle. The concept of instinct should not be confused with the concept of drive. Drives are the great motivators while instincts are their servants. For example, it is self-preservation that compels an animal to seek food. On the other hand, it is the hunting instinct which makes it efficient in seeking food.

The hunting instinct is the predator's ability to run down, catch and kill the prey. Most of our breeds of dog show strong hunting instincts and will run down what they consider to be prey, such as mice, rabbits, the occasional blackbird foraging in our garden, or the unfortunate neighbour's cat. It may also be a hunting instinct which triggers the dog to chase joggers, although this might be explained by allelomimetic behaviour.

It is a misunderstanding to attribute dominance and submission to instinctive origins, as these behaviour patterns are a product of early learning. Popular theories also reduce dog behaviour to a series of distinctive actions, overlooking the complexity of the repertoire of behaviour patterns shown by the dog. The most serious mistake is not realising that the majority of a dog's behaviour is caused by adaptation to environmental stimuli, triggered by motivational factors. As in all higher forms of life, the dog is provided with inborn abilities to perform certain actions as well as the ability to adapt itself to environmental changes.

DRIVE, ETHOLOGY — THE HISTORY OF, LEARNING.

During play, dogs show expressions also registered during serious conflict, slightly modified or lacking intensity. One of the most common behaviour patterns connected with invitation to play is play-bow as shown above.

Invitation to play

Play is very important for young dogs but it is also relevant for adults, even if they don't play as frequently. The function of play is to prepare the youngster for later life and to train it in the skills needed to cope with various situations. Animals' play differs as much as the characteristics of their specific species. Predators play at hunting scenarios, while prey animals play at escaping manoeuvres. Social predators, such as wolf cubs, play socially aggressive games which relate to rank ordering, while social prey animals, such as male lambs, butt each other from as early as one month of age.

Since a great deal of play in dogs is connected with fighting and hunting, it is important for individuals to be able to distinguish between reality and pretence.

During play, dogs show all the expressions also registered during serious conflict, only slightly modified or lacking intensity. The two most common behaviour patterns connected with invitation to play are the play-face and play-bow.

Recent studies have suggested that play has an autonomous motivation, i.e. it is motivated by itself.

PLAY, PLAY-BOW, PLAY-FACE, INFANTILE BEHAVIOUR.

Jacobson's organ

The Jacobson's organ (canalis incisivus) is a channel connecting the nasal cavity with the mouth cavity through the hard palate, with an opening just behind the middle incisors in the upper jaw.

The Jacobson's organ operates by transmitting olfactory information from the mouth cavity to the nasal cavity which means that the dog can taste and smell substances simultaneously.

Males analysing the urine of a female in heat are often seen chattering their teeth and salivating, which facilitates the transmission of smell particles through the Jacobson's organ. This is called a Flehmen response.

NOSE, OLFACTORY IMPRESSION, SCENT, FLEHMEN.

Jealousy

The concept of jealousy implies human values, such as ownership, loyalty, rivalry and self-respect, which are irrelevant from an ethological point of view.

Many behaviours which dog owners usually relate to jealousy can be explained more objectively. The dog showing aggression when the owner greets the family's second dog is not jealous, only maintaining what he perceives as the family's rank order. The other dog is not permitted to make contact with the leader of the pack (the owner) before the higher-ranking dog. Nor is a dog jealous of the new baby in the house, but wishes to keep the rank order clear.

We must remember to avoid anthropomorphic explanations of our dog's behaviour, and in this respect it must be said that even describing dog owners as alpha figures or leaders of the pack may be committing the crime of anthropomorphism.

XENOPHOBIA, RANK ORDER, RANK ORDERING, SOCIAL ANIMALS.

Joy

The dog expresses joy with large, wide eyes, raised and attentive ears and a closed mouth, unless it is so excited that it barks. Joyful dogs adopt a large, stiff body posture and may even make dancing movements with their front paws. The tail wags horizontally, with the exception of the terriers and similar dogs with upright tails, or dogs with permanently curled tails.

The happy and excited dog may alternate rapidly between dominant and submissive postures—it looks determined and friendly in turn.

DOMINANCE, SUBMISSION, FRIENDLINESS.

Juvenile behaviour

Juvenile behaviour is the behaviour displayed by youngsters. Some aspects of it are forms of behaviour which develop certain functions in adulthood. Other parts of juvenile behaviour though seem to be specifically adapted to the survival of the young animal. Common forms of juvenile behaviour are food-soliciting and play.

Juvenile behaviour is the result of genetic predisposition and learning, as is all behaviour, and maturation, which enables youngsters to perform more efficient actions as their motor skills get better in the course of time.

In predatory animals, like the dog, puppies are helpless at birth and show a slow development towards adulthood. Juvenile behaviour, as well as infantile and neonatal behaviour, is well distinguished from adult behaviour. In prey animals, such as horses, sheep and gnu, where the youngster runs with the herd soon after birth, there is not the same range of juvenile traits.

INFANTILE BEHAVIOUR, NEONATAL BEHAVIOUR.

The puppy presses its paws alternately against the mother's teats in order to stimulate her milk production.

Kneading

Kneading is shown when the puppy presses its paws alternately against the mother's teats in order to stimulate her milk production. This behaviour is inborn in the puppy and is extremely important for its survival. In spite of the fact that this is inborn behaviour, puppies get better at performing it with age.

This behaviour is later modified into pawing behaviour, which is an appeal for friendliness, acceptance, and is a pacifying gesture.

PAWING, NEONATAL BEHAVIOUR, REDIRECTED BEHAVIOUR.

Language

There is some controversy over how language should be defined and which criteria should be used to classify a communication system as a language. Normally, language is regarded as a uniquely human feature. To be regarded as language a system must be symbolic, open, able to encompass creative constructions, abstract ideas and the concept of time. Despite the discovery of highly evolved communication systems in other animals, only human language fits the description accurately enough to qualify as a language under this definition.

In the author's opinion it is not useful to talk of the dog's communication system as a true language. Many misunderstandings between dog and owner arise from the fact that owners try to communicate with their dogs by means of human language—and expect the dog to understand them. However, for the purposes of simplicity, the rest of this book refers to the dog's system of communication as language.

COMMUNICATION.

Leadership

Most pack animals have a rank order where there is a number one, the leader of the pack, or the 'alpha' animal, as it is also called. In small packs of wolves the alpha wolf is often the oldest male. The others are his offspring, with exception of the alpha female. In larger packs, the alpha position does not necessarily belong to the eldest member. The leader of the pack is, as a rule, a well-balanced animal who seldom has fights and often solves rank-ordering problems with a display of extremely superior and dominant behaviour.

The alpha wolf achieves its position thanks to experience and its ability to solve the pack's survival problems. Early theories assigned the alpha wolf its rank due to its physical strength and dictatorship in the pack. More recent observations seem to indicate that the leader of the pack is significantly more passive than at first assumed. The alpha wolf does not always get its own way and many relevant functions of the pack are performed by other members. It was also assumed that the alpha wolf always showed dominant facial expressions and body language as well as a high tail carriage, which have now been shown not to be the case. The alpha wolf's role is to keep the pack together, lead it on hunting expeditions, patrol the territory and mark it, as well as carry out various paternal duties. Recent studies also show that there is a significant difference between the behaviour of the alpha wolf in captivity and in the wild.

Some scientists have suggested that the real leader of the pack is the alpha female. Indeed, it is the alpha female which regulates the pack's yearly rhythm of activities, especially during the mating season and until the cubs are three or four months old.

When our dogs form packs rank ordering follows the same principles that are seen in the wild, with some extreme differences which may significantly change the process. For instance, dogs, like other animals in captivity, do not need a leader. The survival of the pack depends on humans, who take care of them. Therefore it often happens that the leader in a dog pack is the strongest, and not the most experienced or intelligent.

It is doubtful whether the dog considers his owner as leader of the pack in the same way that it would regard another dog in the same position. However, we can strive to fulfil such a role if we understand that our leadership cannot be based on fear, but on respect and admiration. This can be done by creating many situations where we show the dog how good we are at solving problems, for example, by hiding food and then giving simple signals to direct the dog towards it.

AGGRESSION, DOMINANCE, STARING, RANK ORDER, RANK ORDERING.

Learning

Learning is the process where the individual answers to changes in the environment with correspondingly changed and adapted behaviour. We have to distinguish between changes in the normal course of behaviour due to motivational factors and to learning. For example, if a wolf passes prey without chasing it, it may be due to the fact that it is not hungry. If, on the other hand, the wolf ignores the prey because it connects it with the early experience of an unsuccessful hunt, this is due to learning. All learning seems to be the ability to connect at least two experiences as cause and effect. In classic conditioning, stimulus and response are connected. In operant conditioning, stimulus and reinforcement are connected. Certain behaviour patterns in dogs may be learned by means of classical conditioning. More complicated sequences of behaviour require greater motivation and the ability of association. We can teach a dog to lie down by reflex, classical conditioning, or by reinforcing the action (operant conditioning), but to teach it to retrieve, we need a longer sequence of positive reinforcements leading towards our goal (shaping).

Dogs will try to solve problems that they are motivated to. They will be learning without our participation. For example, dogs learn to open doors if they are triggered by hunger or need contact. This learning process will be a successive approximation.

Association, i.e. the ability to connect two different experiences as cause and effect,

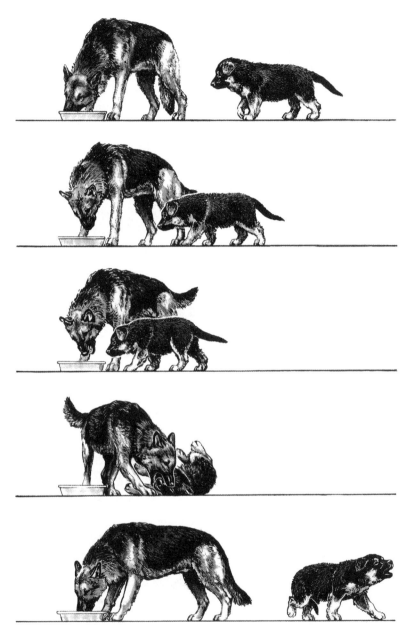

The puppy doesn't know what snarling means. One of the dog mother's most important tasks is to teach the puppy dog language. Sometimes the female seems a bit violent, but she never hurts the puppy.

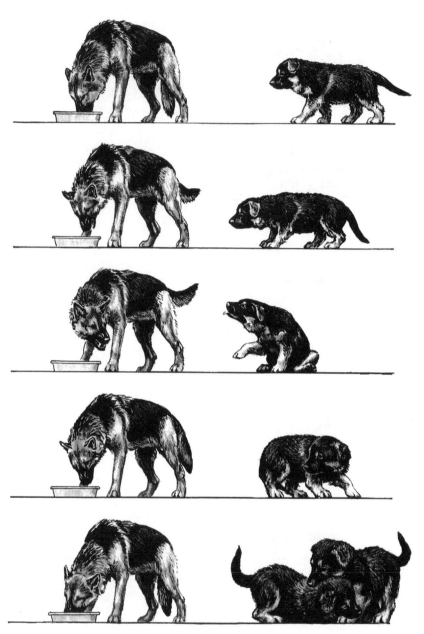

Now the puppy knows the meaning of snarling. The puppy retreats showing pacifying gestures—licking the air, pawing and showing the twist movement— whenever the mother snarls. The puppy then sneaks away and soon will be playing with a sibling. An important lesson is learned.

together with memory and motivation, are necessary conditions for all learning in higher forms of life.

It is through the first contact with the world that infants acquire vital knowledge which later on will make the difference between life and death. Learning that water is wet and fire is hot and contact with hard items brings pain, what tastes good and what doesn't are all achieved through contact with the external world. Such mental knowledge has to be learned by the self—it cannot be read or heard about.

Young animals throw themselves into various unknown situations because their lack of experience means that they don't know the likely outcome. Their curiosity drives them forward while their inborn existential fear restricts their curiosity. A well-balanced relationship between these two factors advances learning at the right pace. This is the first formula for what, hopefully, will be a long life. The infant's curiosity is here called motivation.

Early environmental effects on infants are called imprinting. This learning will remain with it for the rest of its life.

ASSOCIATION, LEARNING THEORIES, IMPRINTING, MOTIVATION, CONDITIONED BEHAVIOUR, OPERANT CONDITIONING, SHAPING, REINFORCEMENT.

Learning theories

Learning happens in various ways. Some authors emphasise one way of learning more than others, but most agree that learning happens mainly through imprinting, conditioning, operant conditioning, shaping and association.

LEARNING, ASSOCIATION, IMPRINTING, CLASSICAL CONDITIONING, OPERANT CONDITIONING, SHAPING.

Leg

Legs obviously have the task of supporting the dog and moving it from one location to another! Different breeds of dog have very different length legs as well as differently developed leg muscles. Some breeds have legs which seem out of pro-portion, either because of the size in relation to their bodies, or other anatomic peculiarities due to our selection of breeding material and occasional mutations. These breeds have been man-made, to satisfy our aesthetic sense, or lack of it.

Legs emphasise body signals. The submissive, fearful or cautious dog walks slowly, with its legs crouched. The dominant or aggressive dog walks on stiff legs.

MOVEMENT.

The submissive, fearful or cautious dog walks slowly, with its legs crouched. The dominant or aggressive dog walks on stiff legs.

Licking

Licking behaviour has its origins in neonatal behaviour when the puppy tries to find its mother's teats to suckle. Suckling is then re-oriented and is used as a pacifying gesture. The insecure or submissive dog licks its adversary. Licking can also be seen as a purely pacifying gesture, even when there is no other dog to lick.

Dog mothers lick their puppies to keep them clean and probably warm as well. This contact may also be relevant in developing the puppies' tactile awareness.

Licking is also seen in connection with courtship behaviour, where the male licks the female's genitals prior to mounting.

PACIFYING BEHAVIOUR, GREETING, MATERNAL BEHAVIOUR, SEXUAL BEHAVIOUR, COMMUNICATION, JACOBSON'S ORGAN.

Life's basic drives

The basic drives of life are self-preservation, aggression and reproduction.

Self-preservation makes use of the strong, inborn mechanisms of fear and hunting (for a predator).

Aggression uses signs and the development of rituals and inhibitions in order that social and aggressive animals can co-exist for mutual benefit.

Reproduction is served by sexual behaviour and parental/nursing behaviour. Both are inborn abilities although they are perfected through practice. Both are under the influence of hormonal stimuli.

SELF-PRESERVATION, AGGRESSION, REPRODUCTION, SEXUAL BEHAVIOUR, DRIVE.

Lip-smacking

Dogs use lip-smacking as a pacifying behaviour. The dog may flick its tongue out of the front of its mouth, showing small licking movements and making gentle lip-smacking noises to pacify an opponent. This behaviour originates from infantile gestures used to solicit food.

LIPS, LICKING.

When a dog snarls with the lips drawn forward, or curled, it shows self-confidence, superiority and dominance. When the dog snarls with its lips drawn back it shows inferiority and submission.

Lips

The lips of the dog can have two extreme positions, either totally drawn forward or drawn back, with several positions in between.

When a dog snarls with the lips drawn forward, or curled, it shows self-confidence, superiority and dominance. This is confirmed by other parts of the body such as the ears or eyes. When the dog snarls with its lips drawn back it shows inferiority and submission which is also confirmed by other behaviour patterns. In both cases the dog is showing aggression.

During various appeasement gestures the dog shows friendliness and/or submission by drawing back its lips.

FACIAL EXPRESSIONS.

Loneliness

Some animals are genetically programmed to live alone, while others seek the company of the same species. Which strategy the animal chooses depends on what favours its survival. Genetic programming is due to an age-old selection process where the fittest survives.

The dog, like the wolf, is a social animal who dislikes being alone. The lonesome wolf howls in order to locate other wolves. Under normal circumstances, a wolf is never alone from birth to death. The lonesome dog howls in exactly the same way and for the same reason. Our dogs therefore need to be trained in order to be able to be left at home alone. Neglecting to train a dog in this way will often result in serious problems later on. Occasionally, fear phobias, perhaps even of a neurotic nature, arise as a result of dogs being left alone. These are difficult to cure.

SOCIAL ANIMALS, HOWL.

Marking

Marking is the behaviour of claiming a territory or an object by leaving your own personal identification mark on it. Dogs frequently mark territory by urinating at trees, lamp-posts etc. Normally, males urinate by cocking one of their hind legs. Marking can also be done by defecating in specific locations. Some dogs also mark visually by scratching the soil with their paws, even on tarmac or cement. This is not an attempt by the dog to clean up after itself.

It is primarily dominant or self-confident individuals who mark. In a pack of wolves it is the leaders who mark the territory. Females may also mark, and some even assume a position similar to a male's—cocking one of their hind legs.

The purpose of marking is to inform other dogs that the territory is inhabited. This is important since conspecifics compete over the same resources, such as food, resting places and mating partners.

TERRITORIAL BEHAVIOUR, DEFECATION, ANAL GLANDS, URINE.

Maternal behaviour

Maternal behaviour is all behaviour shown by the mother towards her offspring. In most species the care-taking of youngsters is done by the mother, and the dog is no exception. Females develop specific behaviour patterns aimed at nursing their youngsters.

Although it is primarily the female who takes care of the puppies, the father and other adults do become interested in the feeding and raising of the puppies at a later stage, if given the opportunity.

Immediately after birth, the mother dries the puppies, keeps them warm, feeds them and licks them clean. The female's maternal behaviour after birth is controlled by hormonal processes and disturbances many occur if the female gives birth too early. Pseudo-pregnancy causes females to undergo hormonal changes eliciting maternal behaviour.

When the puppies become older the mother begins to educate them. She gives them the first lessons in dog language. Growling and snarling is inborn, but puppies need to learn their meaning. Weaning is used as a part of the process of the puppies' education.

The dog mother has a full time job: to feed the puppies—first with milk, and then by regurgitation—to keep them clean and warm—especially when they are very small—an to educate them. Payment? If one puppy succeeds in surviving she will have given the world 50% of her genes.

The mother has three main tasks: 1) To feed the puppies, first with milk, and then by regurgitation, 2) To keep them clean and warm, especially when they are very small, and later to keep their surroundings clean by eating the puppies' faeces, 3) To educate the puppies.

A good mother is patient and diligent. When the puppies grow, dog owners often misunderstand the mother's more apparently violent educational methods. She may growl at them and even attack them, but she never harms them. Without the mother's intervention, the puppies would never become good social animals and would not be able to function in a pack. When the puppies are about 8-10 weeks old the mother seems to lose some of her earlier interest in them.

Dog owners sometimes report problems where the mother has no interest in her puppies, or is too violent towards them. Sometimes she may even kill her offspring. These problems are mainly due to the lack of understanding of the mother's needs during and after birth, and are often a result of stress or insecurity.

NURSERY BEHAVIOUR, PATERNAL BEHAVIOUR, BIOTONUS.

Maternal effect

Maternal effect is the mother's influence at the first stage of her puppies' lives. This can have such an influence on certain behaviour patterns that it can be difficult to distinguish between maternal effect and the effect of genetics. Observations have shown that a female who reacts nervously or fearfully towards certain sounds, for example, may influence her puppies to develop sound phobias even if there is no specific genetic cause.

The influences of maternal effect on puppies' behaviour is the main reason why it is impossible to assess an hereditary co-efficient for specific traits.

MATERNAL BEHAVIOUR, INHERITED BEHAVIOUR.

*Male mounting female after several attempts. See also **sexual behaviour.***

Mating

Mating is referred to by many different expressions, such as, humping, bonking, mounting, copulating etc!

See **Sexual behaviour**.

Memory

Memory is the ability to perform an action which has been previously learned. Even if we frequently use the term unequivocally, it is difficult to give a more precise definition of the word. The reason for this is that memory processes and learning processes are indivisible.

There are three types of memory: 1) Short-term memory, referring to the amount of information which we keep in a period from seconds to a few minutes, as for example when we remember a telephone number from the moment we look it up to the moment we dial it; 2) Middle-term memory refers to information retained by animals in learning experiments during a period of about 24 hours, after which they forget the solution to the problem and increase the rate of mistakes; 3) Long-term memory is what we understand by memory in common language. This is what gives humans and animals the ability to perform behavioural sequences learned a long time previously. It is this type of memory we connect with experience.

Animals' memory is connected with what is vital to the animal as well as certain biological factors. For example, a dog will remember the place where it saw a rabbit far more readily than the place where it saw an attractive young lady driving a Lotus Elan. Dogs always remember people they connect with certain biological processes, for example, those who feed them. Memory—the ability to register and retain information for later utilisation—is indispensable for the development of social behaviour patterns and the survival of the individual.

LEARNING, LEARNING THEORIES, ASSOCIATION.

Misunderstandings between human and dog

Many conflicts between human and dog are caused by misunderstandings of each other's signals. Many dogs have been labelled problem dogs because their owners misunderstand their behaviour, or because they misunderstand their owners. Unpleasant consequences, such as bites, may follow.

When different animals use similar expressions misunderstandings are liable to happen. The human smile shows friendliness, while the chimpanzee shows fear and the wolf expresses aggression.

Both attitudes shown by the children in the above illustration are typical human expression of friendliness. They are also potentially dangerous situations whenever the dogs in question do not understand their meaning in human language. In the upper illustration the boy is decreasing the distance separating him from the fearful dog, which is trying to increase the same distance. In the lower illustration hugging— an expression of affection in humans—may be misinterpreted as dominance with subsequent catastrophic consequences.

A classic situation where a misunderstanding may arise is during greeting, where humans show friendliness towards dogs by smiling, which means opening the mouth and showing the teeth and by out-stretching the hand. This is a human pacifying gesture. Behaviour which once had a certain purpose often becomes ritualised, which means it has lost its practical purpose and has gained a meaning. The out-stretched hand is no longer used to show that we do not carry a weapon, but to show friendliness. Some dogs, especially signal-sensitive or fearful dogs, can misunderstand this greeting ceremony which belongs solely to the human world. The dog understands the situation only from its own point of view. The smile resembles a snarled threat, and the out-stretched hand is seen as a violation of the dog's personal space. This leads the dog to assume a defensive position. If we continue to come closer, the dog will flee if possible, or turn its fear into aggression and bite if there is no escape.

A greeting that the dog understands is the following: ideally you should squat down on your haunches, thereby giving a pacifying gesture with your body. Averting your gaze is seen as friendliness and non-threatening behaviour. Wait until the dog slowly comes and sniffs at you. If the dog is very anxious about the whole encounter it usually helps to make champing movements and noises with your mouth. Champing is recognised as being pacifying for all mammals. When the dog has sniffed you, you can get up slowly. The fact that you are 1.2-1.5 metres taller than the dog will then not be so frightening.

Another common misunderstanding is hugging. Humans, like all primates, hug each other closely. This is a natural and comfortable position for the new-born primate as it is of vital importance to keep close to the mother's breast. There the infant receives milk, warmth and care. For dogs, with a different anatomy from the primates, hugging has another meaning and is connected with either a display of dominance, or mating. Some serious problems between children and dogs have been reported because of this. The child hugs the dog to show affection, but an old dog may perceive it as a dominant act and turn quickly to warn the child. If the dog accidentally hits the child's face with its teeth, the encounter can assume serious consequences. In such a situation we cannot blame either child or dog. The blame lies entirely with the dog owner and parents as well as all other adults who have failed to teach both parties how to interact.

Many dog owners suffer great disappointment because they do not realise that the dog is not able to understand what we say and that it can only react to a set of signals, including sound signals and what we call language. To avoid misunderstandings and to fully exploit the enjoyment of being a dog owner, it is necessary for us to understand that, quite simply, the dog is a dog.

PEOPLE AND DOGS, PACIFYING BEHAVIOUR, GREETING.

Motivation

Motivation is what compels an animal to do what it does. Defined in this way the concept seems simple. However, the scientist must be able to observe the animal's behaviour and changes in behaviour without intervention from subjective factors, preconceived assumptions or theories. Motivation must be able to be explained exclusively by the law of causality: every effect has a cause. But what are the causes? At first, we may answer the question by saying that what motivates the animal are the drives: self-preservation motivates hunting, sex drive motivates mating and aggression motivates the expulsion of the rival. However, the problem is more complicated when we become aware that the drives operate through a complicated system comprising of many behaviour patterns, some of which are inborn while others develop through interactions with the environment.

Motivation is relevant to communication. For example, fear, aggression, dominance/ superiority and submission/inferiority are reflected in most of the dog's facial expressions and body postures. Motivation is also vital when teaching the dog tricks or exercises.

DRIVE, INSTINCT, LEARNING, COMMUNICATION.

Mounting

See **Sexual behaviour** and **Dominance.**

As a rule female dogs are only willing to be mounted by males when their are in heat.

The dominant dog may seize the submissive by the muzzle to emphasize its rank. Notice the submissive dog's posture with laid back ears and raises paw. The dominant dog shows an immense self control in such a situation.

Mouth

Canidae have well-developed teeth and use their mouths primarily to eat and as a tool to grasp objects. In the canine family the mouth often acts as the equivalent of the hand in the primates.

Different expressions of the mouth are used for communication purposes.

LIPS, FACIAL EXPRESSIONS, AGGRESSION, FEAR.

Movement

Most dogs move in three ways: walk, trot and gallop. Some also have a fourth way of moving—an easy or gentle gallop which could be called the canter.

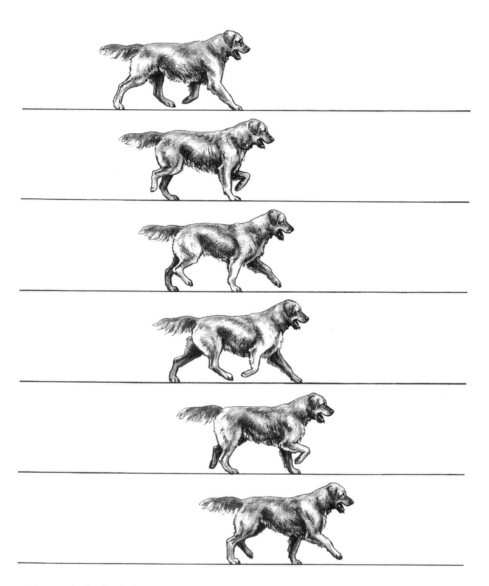

The trot is the dog's favourite gait.

The trot is the dog's favourite gait. Galloping is seldom used and then only for short distances while chasing prey or putting an opponent to flight. Wolves trot daily over great distances, with many short periods of rest or normal walking in between. The wolf's normal walking gait is a unique feature of the species, comprising of quick,

Galloping is seldom used and then only for short distances while chasing prey or putting an opponent to flight.

elegant, springing movements. The wolf has great stamina and can cover many miles in one day at a trotting pace. Most of our dogs can also do this, depending on the breed and size.

Movement demonstrates intention. Generally, the dominant dog walks stiffly, while the submissive one cowers. A relaxed gait reflects peace. Slow, stiff movements are shown immediately prior to attack. Friendly dogs sometimes show small jumping movements while greeting others.

Movement is always combined with facial and bodily attitudes. Behaviour is movement. It is a dynamic process and not a static one.

FACIAL EXPRESSIONS, BODY LANGUAGE, AGGRESSION, FEAR, DOMINANCE, SUBMISSION.

Muzzle-nudge

A muzzle-nudge is where one dog gently nudges another on the muzzle with its own muzzle. It is shows friendliness, acceptance and is a pacifying gesture. Normally, it is a submissive, low-ranking or insecure dog that muzzle-nudges its conspecific.

The muzzle-nudge is a re-directed behaviour pattern. There are two explanations of its origins. The first is that it originates from the puppy's nudging of its mother's teats immediately after birth. The second explanation refers to the pup's nudging of the adult's lips in order to elicit regurgitation. This is seen in puppies from five to seven weeks of age.

The muzzle-nudge may also be used towards humans. Dogs frequently nudge their owner's hand or leg when seeking attention. The muzzle-nudge is also sometimes performed without actual physical contact between the two parties, as a purely pacifying gesture.

MUZZLE TO THROAT, TEAT-NUDGE, REDIRECTED BEHAVIOUR, PACIFYING BEHAVIOUR, FRIENDLINESS, GREETING.

(see illustration page 172)

Muzzle-grasp

During the education of the puppies, the mother often grabs them around the muzzle or head with her mouth, snarling at the same time. This is described as a muzzle-grasp. In the beginning, when the puppies are five to seven weeks old, they

A muzzle-nudge shows friendliness, acceptance and is a pacifying gesture. Normally, it is a submissive, low-ranking or insecure dog that muzzle-nudges its conspecific. The muzzle-nudge is a redirected behaviour pattern. It originates from the pup's nudging of the adult's lips in order to elicit regurgitation.

become very frightened and whimper excessively, even if the mother has not harmed them in any way. Later on, when grasped by the muzzle, the puppy immediately shows passive submission. Earlier, it was assumed that the mother needed to pin the puppy to the ground, but this is not the case as most puppies voluntarily submit. In time, this behaviour pattern assumes variations. Wolf cubs and puppies often invite the alpha male to grasp them by the muzzle. They solicit the dominant male to perform a demonstration of superiority, at the same time showing their acceptance of it and their submission. This is the most reassuring behaviour an adult dog can show a puppy.

This behaviour is also seen in milder forms between adult dogs, either during play or during common social interactions. It can also be seen during conflicts when the dominant dog shows its dominance towards the submissive. However, this behaviour pattern is never seen in serious conflicts.

DOMINANCE, SUBMISSION, MATERNAL BEHAVIOUR, PATER-NAL BEHAVIOUR.

Muzzle to throat

See **Nose to throat**.

Neck

Various positions of the neck are used as part of facial or body postures.

NECK POSITIONS, INHIBITIONS.

Turning the head away, with the throat exposed as a consequence, demonstrates a refusal to look the opponent in the eye. This behaviour shows submission, fear, or both. Exposing the throat and lying on the back at the same time is a pacifying gesture. It means submission and surrender.

Neck positions

The dominant dog holds its neck straight. The submissive dog inclines its neck, at the same time turning its eyes away from its opponent and cringing. Turning the head away and exposing the throat means friendliness and is a pacifying gesture. When a dominant dog exposes its throat it shows it accepts its opponent's submission and that it has no intention of taking further action. When a submissive dog does the same it means that it accepts the other's higher rank.

Exposing the throat and lying on the back at the same time is a pacifying gesture as well. It means submission and surrender. Turning the head away, with the throat exposed as a consequence, demonstrates a refusal to look the opponent in the eye. This behaviour shows submission, fear, or both.

Konrad Lorenz interpreted such posturing as inhibiting the opponent's bite. He described the action of exposing the soft and vulnerable parts of the body as inhibiting the attacker, after studying similar behaviour in birds. Although this may be partially true, there is another explanation. Lying on the back is closely connected with a behaviour first seen in the puppy's early days when the mother overturns it to lick its belly. Over-turning and exposing the belly could therefore be a redirected behaviour pattern from this original action.

THROAT, FACIAL EXPRESSIONS, BODY LANGUAGE, FEAR, AGGRESSION.

Negative reinforcement

A negative reinforcement is an event which when withdrawn increases a certain behaviour. In other words, a reinforcement which consists of terminating stimuli is called a negative reinforcement. For instance, if every time a dog barks it is sprayed with water and the dog stops barking in order to avoid being sprayed, then the water spray is a negative reinforcement.

REINFORCEMENT, OPERANT CONDITIONING, POSITIVE REINFORCEMENT.

Neonatal behaviour

The new-born's behaviour is called neonatal behaviour. (Greek, neos = new, Latin, natalis = birth.)

For puppies, milk, warmth and care are the most important factors for their survival. Right from birth, the puppy is therefore designed to cope with these demands.

Kneading is the behaviour used by the puppy to stimulate milk production. It consists of alternate pressing with the front paws close to the mother's nipple. The ability to suckle and the suckle reflex makes the puppy an extremely efficient little mammal. If someone puts a finger in the puppy's mouth, it will suckle intensely on the finger, even to the extent that it can cling on to the finger by its mouth when lifted. If the puppy is left alone on a table it will begin crawling, while making typical pendulum head movements from side to side. This helps the puppy to move in circles. If there is anything warm in close proximity, such as the mother or a human hand, the puppy will find it and will press itself against it for warmth.

Unlike piglets, puppies do not have favourite teats. They seem to shift between the rear nipples where the milk production is greatest and the front ones, closer to the mother's head where it is easier for her to lick them and help them with their digestion, defecation and urination.

In the neonatal period, the puppy is totally concerned with suckling, digesting and sleeping. The puppy cannot see, but it is not isolated from the exterior world. Impressions are registered all the time and the puppy is constantly under the influence of imprinting. What will later seem to it as being natural or unnatural, an inclination or aversion, are strongly connected with these first influences. A human hand warming the puppy for a couple of minutes each day is initially enough to imprint them on to humans. Human voices while the puppy drowsily suckles will later be connected with pleasure.

At birth, the puppy is undeveloped in comparison with, for instance, a lamb. Sheep have evolved to be so well developed at birth that they can follow their parents in their eternal search for grazing areas almost immediately. Puppies, on the other hand, are born undeveloped so they can remain in the den without drawing attention to themselves while their parents are out hunting. This difference is so important from an evolutionary point of view that all predators use this strategy.

Puppies seem helpless at birth and for the first couple of weeks, yet they are totally equipped for life ahead.

MATERNAL BEHAVIOUR, INFANTILE BEHAVIOUR, PRECOCIAL ANIMAL, ALTRICIAL ANIMAL.

Neonatal behaviour—for puppies, milk, warmth and care are the most important factors for their survival. Right from birth, the puppy is therefore designed to cope with these demands. Puppies seem helpless at birth and for the first couple of weeks, yet they are totally equipped for life ahead.

Neurosis

Neuroses (Greek, neuron = nerve, osis = condition) are psychiatric cases or functional derangements, where irrational reactions are seen in rational individuals. These are often seen after a strain that the individual's reference system cannot cope with. Neuroses are not caused by organic change. There is much controversy about whether animals can suffer from neuroses or whether the term can be meaningfully applied to animal behaviour disorders. If it can, then the most common example of neurotic behaviour in dogs is caused by separation anxiety.

Neuroses can often be cured with the help of medicine and psychotherapeutic programmes in combination.

PATHOLOGICAL BEHAVIOUR, REFERENCE SYSTEM, FEAR, AGORAPHO-BIA, CLAUSTROPHOBIA.

The dog is genetically programmed to use its nose. The brain centres dealing with olfactory signals are well developed in all canids.

Normal behaviour

Normal behaviour is behaviour which is qualitatively and quantitatively shown on average by a certain species and population in a defined period of time, towards specific stimuli, where all common elements exist.

The concept of normal behaviour is, from an ethological point of view, always connected with population and a period of time. What is normal or purposeful at a certain time can depend on environmental changes. We must always use average observations to determine what is normal behaviour since behaviour is quantitative and not qualitative. All animals in a certain population have the same repertoire of behaviour patterns, but some show certain patterns more than others.

PATHOLOGICAL BEHAVIOUR, SELECTION.

Nose

See **Scent.**

A submissive dog may poke its dominant adversary in the side of the throat with its nose. It shows acceptance of the other's dominance.

Nose to throat

A submissive dog may nudge or poke its dominant adversary in the side of the throat with its nose. This behaviour is a sort of muzzle-nudge but is directed at the throat. It shows acceptance of the other's dominance and is a pacifying gesture.

A variation on this behaviour is a nudge to the other's ear, rather than their throat.

'Nose to throat' is also seen without physical contact, when the submissive dog nudges in the air and general direction of the dominant dog, but does not touch it. Normally this is seen in combination with other displays such as lowering of the head, leg twists and low tail wagging.

MUZZLE-NUDGE, PACIFYING BEHAVIOUR.

In a normal dog or wolf pack, most of the adults will show interest and care towards puppies once they reach a certain age.In showing nursery behaviour towards the pups they are protecting their own genes.

Nursery behaviour

In a normal dog or wolf pack, most of the adults will show interest and care towards puppies once they reach a certain age, leave the den and begin showing playful behaviour. This is very adaptive from a genetic point of view. All members of the pack share a certain number of genes from the same gene pool.

MATERNAL BEHAVIOUR, PATERNAL BEHAVIOUR.

Oestrus

Oestrus, season, or heat, depends on hormonal changes which prepares the female's system for mating and reproduction. The female's behaviour can change during oestrus. Normally, she will be more inviting towards males and more aggressive towards females.

Sometimes a female's behaviour changes so much during oestrus that medical treatment is required.

The name oestrus originates from the 'ox warble fly', which is a very strong, very hairy, bi-winged insect. The larvae live in mammals but the adults do not eat throughout their lives. They bite cattle however, which consequently react by becoming very excited. The Latin name for this insect is Oestrus (family Oestridiae), and after the discovery of its bite's consequences on cattle behaviour, the name oestrus began to be used to designate the period where the female is ready for reproduction and shows excited sexual behaviour.

SEXUAL BEHAVIOUR, SEASON, PHANTOM PREGNANCY, PATHOLOGICAL BEHAVIOUR.

The female's behaviour can change during oestrus. Normally, she will be more inviting towards males and more aggressive towards females.

Older dogs

Older dogs show the same behaviour as young dogs. The only differences are where the dog's senses fail. For example, loss of sight or hearing changes the way the dog investigates its world and it may develop an increasing alertness in some situations.

Older dogs can learn new tricks but more time may be needed and more repetitions required. Older dogs still need to be activated and need physical exercise, too.

Olfactory impression

Olfactory impression means smell impression.

SCENT, JACOBSON'S ORGAN.

Olfactory signals

See **Scent signals**

Ontogenesis

Ontogenesis (Greek, ontos = to be; genesis = birth) is the development from birth to the adult state. It describes the origins and development of an individual. A specific behaviour pattern's ontogeneisis is the history of this pattern's development from its first form to the present form, through modification, redirections and ritualisation.

PHYLOGENESIS, REDIRECTED BEHAVIOUR, RITUALS.

Operant conditioning

Operant conditioning is based on operants. An operant is something which changes someone's behaviour, or influences the environment. Reinforcements are operants. If an event following a response increases the response's frequency, then that event is a reinforcement. There is a higher probability that a response which is reinforced will be repeated. Reinforcements are necessary to condition operant behaviour in the same way as two stimuli are necessary to condition a reflex behaviour. There isn't however, any stimulus in operant conditioning. Reinforcements are operant events or stimuli which increase the frequency of a certain response, and they may be positive or negative.

In operant conditioning, positive and negative reinforcements are used —not rewards and punishments. However, the definitions and use of these concepts vary between American, British and Scandinavian behaviourists.

LEARNING, CONDITIONED BEHAVIOUR, REINFORCEMENT, POSITIVE REINFORCEMENT, NEGATIVE REINFORCEMENT, REFLEX.

Over-stimulation

See **Hyperactivity.**

Pacifying behaviour

Pacifying behaviour (Latin pacificarae, of or from pax = peace and facere = to make) is all behaviour with the purpose of suppressing an opponent's aggression.

Pacifying behaviour in dogs is closely related to initial friendliness and submission or inferiority, and then with fear. The differences between pacifying, friendly, fearful or submissive behaviour are, generally, small and quantitative.

Some pacifying behaviour has its origins in neonatal and infantile behaviour and only becomes pacifying behaviour through redirection and eventually ritualisation. Examples of this are pawing, the muzzle-nudge and twist movements.

Other forms of pacifying behaviour rely on concealing all signs of aggression, such as when the dog closes its mouth and looks away from its opponent. Sexual behaviour can also be pacifying. The dog that turns its back on its opponent hides all signs of aggression, concealing its head, eyes and teeth while also attempting to change the opponent's aggression into sexual motivation.

Pacifying behaviour is learned by puppies and wolf cubs at a very early age; from about six weeks onwards. It is very important for puppies or cubs to be able to pacify or appease adults when they begin interacting with them, by appealing to their parental behaviour.

FACIAL EXPRESSIONS, BODY LANGUAGE, INFANTILE BEHAVIOUR, NEONATAL BEHAVIOUR, REDIRECTED BEHAVIOUR, RITUALS, PAWING, MUZZLE-NUDGE, TWIST MOVEMENT.

Pack

A pack is a group of animals of the same species who stick together for various purposes. It is not enough for a group of animals of the same species, in the same place, at the same time, to be called a pack. In a wolf pack, for example, there is a strong bond between the different members. Strangers, or other members of the same species, are not automatically accepted when meeting a new pack. Acceptance by the pack only occurs after many elaborate rituals and ceremonies.

PACK STRUCTURE, PACK ANIMAL.

Pack animal

A pack animal is an animal which lives in a structured group of conspecifics. There are three types of animals in the canine family, depending on the form of society they adhere to: the solitary hunter, the small family animal and the pack animal.

The solitary hunter, such as the Red fox, lives alone for most of the year. In winter it finds a partner and mates. When the young are born the mother stays with them, providing them with food, warmth and contact until they are big enough to be able to survive on their own. The male leaves after mating to return to his solitary existence. Females sometimes establish communities where they look after their youngsters together, although adult female foxes are usually solitary.

The Golden jackal is a family canine. The jackal family usually comprises of a father, mother and offspring. Sometimes one of the yearlings stays in the family to baby-sit the younger siblings. This has been proved to be a successful strategy, since puppies with baby-sitters have greater chances of survival than those without. Jackal groups are always small and the male and female usually stay together for their entire life.

The wolf, the Cape Hunting Dog and the Dingo are large pack canines. A wolf pack may contain two or three individuals, or ten to fifteen. Usually, the well-functioning pack has five to seven members in it. The solitary wolf seeks company and if it is successful in finding another will probably stay with it.

The difference between animals who build different communities is genetic. Adaptation to the environment has forced certain animals to co-operate in order to survive and the best at co-operating have the best chance of mating and spreading their co-operative genes in the population's genetic pool. Selection has thus favoured certain animals to become solitary hunters and others to become pack hunters, depending on environmental and food resources. Combined with this process, co-operative animals were forced to develop certain characteristics such as the ability to communicate and settle conflicts in a relatively safe way. The jackal, for example, uses more facial and bodily expressions than the fox, whose social behaviour patterns are very stereotypical. In the wolf we observe even more detailed communication patterns than the jackal, which seems to indicate that the development of communication patterns are dependent on the social pressures which the animal experiences.

Like the wolf, our domestic dogs are pack animals, which means they possess a great portion of genes programming them to develop social characteristics, enabling them to use specific signals and to understand others' messages. When man domesticated the dog, we favoured the animals that served us best. We chose the animals containing the best genetic possibilities to develop communication with man. Evidence of this is the fact that dogs are much keener to communicate by sound and are usually much noisier than the wolf. Wolves rarely use barking to communicate with each other. However, man is the noisiest living being on earth, so it is no surprise that man's best friend, the dog, should have also become noisier than its ancestor, the wolf.

PACK STRUCTURE, PACK, EVOLUTION.

Pack structure

There are specific patterns and rituals in the establishment of a dog's family pack. The resulting structure is sometimes very complicated. The smallest possible pack is made up of two individuals; a male and a female. It is not unusual to see two young male wolves wandering together, but under normal circumstances, they do not form a pack since they will join a bigger group as soon as this is a viable option, or they will take others into their little group. On the other hand, a group comprising a male and a female may be a stable pack only awaiting expansion of their family. Later on, they will set up a bigger pack with their offspring. It is probable that this is the way most wolf packs have been created.

The study of wolf packs has given us many explanations about canine social behaviour and pack structure. In the period up to the young female's second or third season, conflicts may arise between the old female and her daughter. This may result in young females leaving the pack, sometimes followed by a brother. If the females are older, it is possible that the alpha female will not be able to stand her ground and she may be forced to leave the pack. When this occurs, several young males are keen to accompany her and even the alpha male may go with her. A new pack is then formed and the old pack is split in two.

Conflicts between males are also likely, especially during the females' seasons when the youngsters have become so big that they dare to threaten each other. Eventually, reaching full sexual maturity, they will also threaten other adult males. If the conflicts really escalate, the alpha male may be forced to leave the pack, usually accompanied by a couple of young females, or one or two of his younger sons. In this instance, it is unlikely that the old female will follow him, as he has fallen from grace in his own pack. Normally, she will prefer the safety of her own pack—a sensible choice, since she will probably give birth to cubs a couple of months later.

If a single wolf is ousted from the pack, he will stay on the periphery of the pack for a period and nourish himself on left-overs. If he comes too close to the others he will be chased away. Such a wolf is seldom successful in being accepted again by the

Jackals live in small families with one male, one female, pups and eventually one yearling. Hunting dogs live in larger packs like wolves and dingos.

Fox, jackal and wolf.

pack. After some time he will most probably walk away and will become a lone wolf. If he is fortunate and meets another lone wolf, they may wander together and even establish a pack if they are of opposite sex. These wolves have to be extremely lucky to succeed in setting up a pack and expanding their family. In most cases, lone wolves which have been exiled from the pack will wander around skinny and miserable, until they eventually die. Young wolves are more likely to become periphery wolves than older ones.

In our domestic dogs we see the same patterns for pack structure and pack ordering as the wolf's, but these are usually less extreme. Dog owners should be aware that they cannot expect to acquire a new dog and assume that the old dog will accept the new family member without reservations. Usually, it takes time and a couple of fairly serious conflicts before the old dog accepts the new one. If fights are too violent, perhaps even bloody, owners ought to separate them. In the wild, two such individuals would never establish a pack and we force them into fighting when we insist on having them under the same roof. This situation is rarely resolved.

In traditional training classes we often see a great deal of conflict between dogs. The owners believe that their dogs should regard all the others as a pack after they have been together for two or three lessons, which is certainly not the case. A pack is established when the individuals need each other and when they support each other in the performance of vital daily functions. They learn familiarity with each other through daily routines and create exclusive rituals. These rituals are very important in maintaining the relationships in the pack and a stable rank order. Many times each day, the various members of the pack assure each other that nothing has changed—dominant or submissive positions are still prevailing and stability is maintained. None of this takes place in a training class, where there is not one pack, but 12 or 15 packs made up of two members each—one dog and one owner.

PACK, PACK ANIMAL.

Pain

Pain is registered by sensory cells. Nerve impulses are sent to the brain, which in turn sends messages to the rest of the body for quick action. Pain often causes a reflex action; the pain elicits a specific avoidance response. The stress mechanism of an individual in pain is also alerted, providing the individual with all possible resources to withstand pain. Experiments investigating pain thresholds seem to show that dogs are better than humans in withstanding pain, but this is probably due to the fact that dogs do not seem to experience self-pity.

It is proven that pain, as well as punishment, has no effect whatsoever on learning, and is therefore an expression of our ignorance.

LEARNING THEORIES, PUNISHMENT.

Parental care

See **Maternal behaviour, Paternal behaviour, Nursery behaviour.**

Passive submission

See **Submission.**

Paternal behaviour: The cubs greet their wolf father with exaggerated submissive behaviour. They lick its lips and bite him gently. The wolf father shows acceptance with laid back ears, half closed eyes and great patience. Perhaps he will regurgitate a bit of food to the cubs. Perhaps he will gently grasp a cub around the muzzle with his strong teeth, that only one hour before were used to seize and kill a prey double as big as him self. The wolf father doesn't hurt the cubs—it only shows them that they can trust him.

Paternal behaviour

Paternal behaviour (Latin pater = father) means fatherly behaviour. In dogs and wolves paternal behaviour is not necessarily dependant on the animal becoming a father, but is likely to be displayed simply if the animal is given the opportunity to assume such a role.

Males showing parental behaviour towards puppies are generally well-balanced, superior, experienced males.

The difference between paternal and maternal behaviour is that while maternal behaviour is partly controlled by hormonal processes related to birth and lactation, paternal behaviour is elicited solely by the infantile image of the puppies. Furthermore, there is an important difference in that the role of the mother cannot be performed by another, i.e. birth and lactation, but the role of the father can easily be performed by every male.

The father's primary educational role takes place from the puppies' seventh week of age, until they are adolescents. Like the mother, he is responsible for teaching 'dog language' and for the pups' integration in the rank order of the pack. He may be a bit rough towards them, but he is never violent and he can be extremely patient and caring.

The father's behaviour towards the mother near parturition is very important. The male carries food home to the female and defends the territory more intensely than normal. This is partially controlled by the female's behaviour, as she provokes him constantly. For example, she does not allow him to come into the den. The male's aggression is especially relevant after the birth of the puppies since he will be prepared to defend them constantly.

In domestic dogs, the father's role has almost lost its function as a parent and educator, which the author believes is a mistake from a selection point of view. Male dogs are no longer required to prove their parental skills. If the genes which determine these behaviour patterns also influence other behaviours, such as social disposition or social sensitivity—anability to perceive others' signals—then we are breeding inferior animals.

Experiments conducted by the author at the Etologisk Institute have shown that puppies' social behaviour is influenced by the presence of the father or other adult males from an age of six to seven weeks of age until six to seven months. Statistical results of these experiments were however, inconclusive. No significant correlations were obtained since the available sample was too small.

MATERNAL BEHAVIOUR, PARENTAL CARE, INFANTILE BEHAVIOUR, REGURGITATION.

Pathological behaviour

Pathological behaviour (Greek pathos = disease and logos = justification for, science of) is all behaviour which quantitatively and qualitatively differs from the average behaviour of individuals of a certain species, race and population at a given period of time, or where specific behavioural forms lack a behavioural sequence.

It is important to define behaviour as an average, as there are always individual differences. It is also important to limit definitions to certain groups of individuals, as the prevailing conditions may differ from those acting upon the genetic programme of another population, thus making their behaviour change and adapt in different ways.

In dogs, most cases of pathological behaviour are concerned with fear and aggression. It is normal for dogs to display aggression or fear under certain circumstances and according to well-defined behaviour sequences. If some steps in a sequence are missing, or the triggering factors differ radically from average factors, this behaviour is called pathological. For example, adult dogs which bite or harm puppies show pathological behaviour, since this is not the case for the average population of adult dogs. A dog which attacks without going through a sequence of displays of increasing threat is pathological as well.

Pathological behaviour may sometimes be curable by combining therapy programmes, e.g. behaviour modification programmes, with appropriate medicine.

NORMAL BEHAVIOUR, PSYCHOTIC BEHAVIOUR, NEUROSIS.

The submissive dog lifts its paw as a pacifying gesture.

Pawing

Pawing is the behaviour of touching or striking someone or something with a paw. This pattern can also be observed as intentional, i.e. without actually touching anything or anyone but just indicating an intention. This is especially seen when a submissive dog greets a dominant one from a distance or when a submissive, fearful dog tries to pacify an opponent.

Pawing is a pacifying gesture, a redirected behaviour, a ritualised pattern of the original kneading to stimulate the mother's milk production.

Dog owners are liable to observe this behaviour during training situations where the dog does not understand what they want and paw in the air from sheer frustration. This is an attempt to pacify their owners who may have become impatient.

PACIFYING BEHAVIOUR, REDIRECTED BEHAVIOUR, RITUALS, KNEADING.

Paws

See **Pawing.**

Penis

When a dog shows insecurity or submission its penis can sometimes be seen protracted. This is probably a sexual displacement behaviour.

People and dogs

People and dogs have many opportunities for mutual understanding. Both species have the ability to adapt to the environment, to co-operate with each other and with individuals of other species. Man and dog are both mammals, social animals, hunters, use 'language', are aggressive and perform rituals. It may even be possible that during a certain period of development man and dog had a need to co-operate with one another. It is conceivable that this co-operation began after the last Ice Age, 14, 000 years ago, and that it was a significant factor in the survival of members of both species in certain regions.

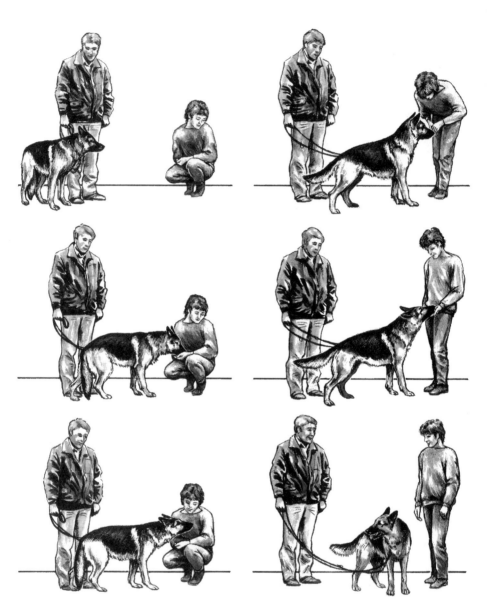

Greeting exercise for shy dogs—We must remove all possible signs of aggression from our bodily expressions. In the beginning the girl in the illustration appears small to he dog and turns her head away. The dog then approaches her and eventually eats the treat she keeps in her hand. Finally, step by step, the dog gets accustomed to the stranger and she may now stand up and show normal human behaviour. This exercise has to be repeated with several strangers to the dog.

As a social animal, and especially as a social hunter, man and dog have both developed complex communication patterns. The best individuals are not the best at individual performances, but those which are best at perceiving and understanding others' movements, signals and at co-ordinating their own actions in response. When they learn each other's signals, man and dog can co-operate efficiently. The high degree of aggression that both possess enables them to build strong dependence on each other and ritualise their aggression in bonding ceremonies.

However, we must be careful not to assume that a good relationship between man and dog is always automatic. In spite of all our similarities there are decisive differences between the two species that can cause fatal misunderstandings.

The dog began by having a working relationship with humans, but now, close to the 21st century, the dog's role is mostly as a pet or companion. The dog is now a substitute for other forms of company: the need to touch a warm body, the object of our frustrated parental behaviour, our last bastion in a relationship with the wilderness. In recent years the dog has also been used successfully as a part of therapeutic psychiatric programmes in the treatment of autistic children, and the elderly etc.

Canis lupus became Canis familiaris—later, Canis civicus, Canis over-familiaris, and then Canis therapeuticus. What will be next?!...

MISUNDERSTANDINGS BETWEEN PEOPLE AND DOGS, RITUALS.

Phantom pregnancy

See **False pregnancy**.

Phenocopy

Phenocopy (Greek, phaino/phainein = show/reveal, Latin, copia = abundance) is a change in the phenotype which is not inherited, but is caused by external factors.

PHENOTYPE.

Phenotype

Phenotype (Greek, phaino/phainen = show/reveal, typos or tupos = impression/figure) means the set of observable characteristics determined by the genotype and the environment. For example, a black-coloured coat in the Cocker Spaniel is the dog's phenotype. The dog is black, but may have the genetic disposition for red. This genetic disposition is called the genotype.

GENOTYPE, GENETICS.

Pheromones have a lot to say when the male sniffs to the female in heat.

Pheromone

Pheromone (Greek, phero = convey, mone from hormone) is a substance secreted or released for detection and response by another animal of the same species, causing a specific reaction or a specific sequence of behaviour. For example, certain female pheromones trigger the male's sexual behaviour. The expression was introduced in 1959 by Karlson and Luschir.

SCENT, PHYSIOLOGY, HORMONES.

Phobia

Phobia (Greek, phobia = fear) is a morbid fear or aversion, or a neurotic fear. For instance, dogs may show hydrophobia (Greek, hydor = water), a fear of water.

FEAR, PATHOLOGICAL BEHAVIOUR, NEUROSIS.

Phylogenesis

Phylogenesis (Greek, phylon = race/tribe, genesis = origins/creation) is the history of a certain species' general development—the evolution of low forms to high forms.

Physiology

Physiology (Greek, physis = nature, logia/logos = justification/science) is the science of the constitution and function of living organisms, their parts and substances. Animal behaviour is under the influence of physiological processes, but there is no conclusive answer as to just how much single elements contribute to specific traits. Some authors are of the opinion that all behaviour can be explained by referring to physiological functions and malfunctions.

Sexual behaviour is an example of physiologically determined behaviour. It is the physiological process of oestrus that causes the animals to show sexual behaviour. There is an interchange between several factors: a genetic disposition triggers physiological processes when and if certain environmental conditions are available. For instance, whether female wolves come into oestrus depends on factors such as time of the year, light, temperature, available food and the social structure of the pack. Our domestic dogs show similar dependence on a series of factors which trigger oestrus. It is not unusual for females dogs who live in a family environment they perceive as unstable to postpone or totally miss an oestrus.

BEHAVIOUR THEORIES, HORMONES, PHEROMONE.

Play

Play is a serious activity. When we connect play with leisure activities or hobbies, we overlook the important role that play has for young animals.

Play behaviour in dogs confirms its importance. Expressions like 'play-face' show how motivation changes from aggression to fear, dominance to submission, and yet none of the participants ever dominates the activity long enough to become overly serious and end the game.

It is through play that puppies learn to know themselves, their abilities to control the environment, and their limits. Through play, puppies learn dog language by con-necting their own and their conspecifics' expressions with the behaviour that occurs

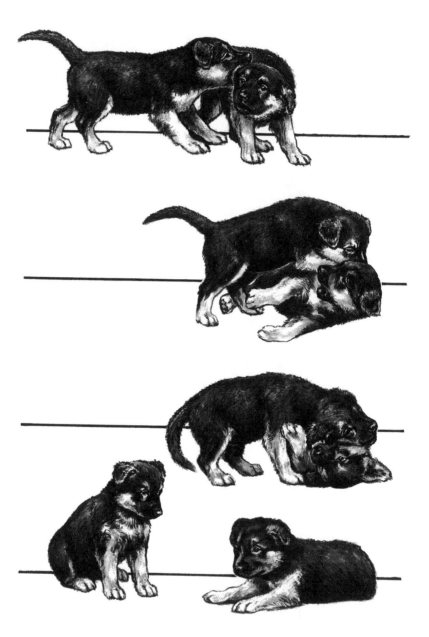

Play is serious—it is through play that young animals learn about their environment, their own strength and weakness, their prey, pack members, etc...

next. Through play puppies also experience conflicts which would have catastrophic consequences if they were meant seriously. The puppy bites its siblings and is bitten in return. The puppy jumps on and over all sorts of obstacles and tries to solve impossible problems. The consequences of all this is that the puppy is learning vital information about itself and its surroundings. Later in life, there isn't a place for such mistakes and misjudgements. Survival in nature depends on momentary and accurate assessments. Even though our puppies may not be faced with life and death judgements in adult life, the seriousness of play behaviour and its purpose has been genetically preserved throughout the generations.

Play also has a role in adult dogs, mainly as a way of trying new strategies which would be risky to try in real situations. Play also allows the adult dog licence by showing infantile behaviour. Body contact with conspecifics, which would normally be prohibited, can occur in play without further consequences.

The origins and consequences of play are not yet fully explained, but many new ideas have recently been put forward. Play seems to be self-motivated. Cats, for example, continue to hunt, not because they are hungry, but because they seem to derive pleasure from the actual act of hunting. If it can be argued that cats hunts for fun, not just when hungry, play can be argued to be self-motivating, since the knowledge obtained through it is of vital importance.

Dog owners should allow their puppies to play with other puppies and learn important aspects of dog life which will later enable them to meet other dogs without problems. The ability to learn dog and human language, and to compromise, can only be learned in company, so puppies should also be allowed to play with adult dogs and children. Children and dogs must always be supervised when playing together.

CHILDREN AND DOGS, PLAY-BOW, PLAY-FACE, INFANTILE BEHAVIOUR, MOTIVATION.

Play-bow

The play-bow is the posture used by a dog to invite another to play. The dog pretends to attack the opponent. It positions the front part of its body as if lying down, with its back end in the air, waits a moment and then jumps playfully at its playmate. The play-face is normally observed in conjunction with the play-bow.

The play-bow is also seen during courtship behaviour. Both male and female may use it as part of courting behaviour.

PLAY, PLAY-FACE, INFANTILE BEHAVIOUR.

Play face to the left and play-bow to the right—both expressions are usually seen during play activity.

Play-face

Play-face is often seen in dogs soliciting another to play. The expression resembles a dominant face, though with retracted lips and erect ears—in the breeds where this is possible.

Play-face behaviour is interesting as it gives us the clue to understanding the true nature of play. It combines expressions normally seen during displays of dominance as well as submission, and even aggression and fear. This is due to the fact that play is a result and a mixture of various motivational factors. The dog pretends that it is aggressive, but it is not. It is dominant and submissive, self-confident and insecure, all at the same time, or rather, interchanging extremely quickly. The motivation of the playful dog changes very quickly, sustaining the whole behaviour as playful activity. If one of the motivational factors is allowed to govern play behaviour a fraction too long, play may then go over into seriousness or even conflict.

Play-face may be used as a displacement behaviour and in courtship behaviour.

PLAY, PLAY-BOW, MOTIVATION, DISPLACEMENT ACTIVITY, COURTSHIP BEHAVIOUR.

Pointing

Pointing is the display that some breeds of gundog show when they stand immobile, usually with a front leg raised and looking forward in the direction of game.

This stance is seen in nearly all wild canids and in many dog breeds, not just gundogs. Predators need to approach prey very carefully, weighing up every move. Pointing, as we see it in our gundog breeds, is an exaggeration of the original natural stance, emphasised by selective breeding.

HUNTING, SELECTIVE BREEDING.

Pointing, as we see it in our gundog breeds, is an exaggeration of the original natural stance, emphasised by selective breeding.

Positive reinforcement

A positive reinforcement is everything which reinforces a certain behaviour when presented. For example, if giving a dog a treat every time it sits increases the rate at which the dog shows that behaviour, then the treat is a positive reinforcement. Positive reinforcements must be presented simultaneously or immediately after the act has taken place.

REINFORCEMENT, OPERANT CONDITIONING, NEGATIVE REINFORCEMENT.

Precocial animal

A precocial animal is one that can feed itself as soon as it is born.

NEONATAL BEHAVIOUR, ALTRICIAL ANIMAL.

Predatory behaviour

The main source of food for a predator is the prey that the animal has caught for itself. Predatory behaviour is therefore of vital importance and has been developed towards specific goals.

Predatory behaviour comprises of searching, possibly tracking, stalking, selecting prey, running it down, killing it and occasionally transporting it to a safe place.

Searching, and possibly tracking, is the most time consuming of the above-mentioned elements and requires a well-developed sense of smell, concentration, experience and stamina. Commonly, there are terrain difficulties to overcome. Wolves can wander day after day, searching or tracking prey. They move at a fast, elegant and springing trot.

When prey is located, they stalk it, even though this phase of the hunt does not assume the same importance in wolves as in solitary predators where the moment of surprise is decisive. Social predators find it more difficult to make successful surprise manoeuvres on their targets. Usually, wolves run round their prey to isolate a single animal and surround it. During this phase of the hunt, co-operation is very important. A wolf seldom attacks prey from the front. While one or two wolves distract the prey, it is attacked by a third wolf from behind.

The killing technique of the wolf is exhaustion by repeatedly biting the prey and retreating. The prey does not die of strangulation, a technique used by feline predators, but may bleed to death. Usually, the prey will die of shock before this happens.

A hunt may take several hours and some have been known to take several days. Usually, wolves consume their prey on the spot, with the higher ranking eating first. Sometimes they transport the carcass to a place where they feel more safe.

If we compare the wolf and dog, there often seems to be a dog breed which is better than the wolf in performing a certain function. However, as a whole, the wolf is much more skilful. Our dog breeds have the same hunting abilities as the wolf but they vary greatly from breed to breed. They have become specialised in restricted areas of this behaviour. For example, the gundog's hunting abilities are no better or worse than the wolf's, they are simply more specialised.

A wolf seldom attacks prey from the front. While one or two wolves distract the prey, it is attacked by a third wolf from behind. The killing technique of the wolf is exhaustion by repeatedly biting the prey and retreating. A hunt may take several hours and some have been known to take several days.

Hunting, or predatory behaviour, is triggered by hunger. It serves the drive of self-preservation. It has nothing whatsoever to do with aggression.

PREDATORY BEHAVIOUR—INHERITANCE OF, DRIVE, INSTINCT, GUNDOGS.

Predatory behaviour—Inheritance of

The inheritance of predatory behaviour traits follows the same rules of inheritance as all forms of behaviour. It depends on genetic disposition, and is influenced by environmental factors.

Popular opinion assumes that hunting behaviour is especially associated with gundogs and dogs specially bred for these abilities. This is not true. Hunting behaviour is so important for predators that it is almost certainly regulated by a great number of genes in different loci (locations in the DNA molecule). A dog totally lacking a predisposition for hunting behaviour would certainly not survive long after birth since other vital functions would then also be damaged.

Selective breeding has perfected some breeds' hunting abilities to suit human needs.

PREDATORY BEHAVIOUR, GUNDOGS, DNA.

Problem dog

A problem dog is a dog that shows behaviour which does not correspond to its owner's expectations. The most common reasons for a dog to become a problem are under-stimulation, a lack of ability on behalf of the owner in gaining the dog's respect, and lack of training in specific situations, e.g. training the dog to cope with being left alone at home.

UNDER-STIMULATION, HYPERACTIVITY, LEADERSHIP.

Protean behaviour

Protean behaviour (from the Greek hero Proteus, who, according to legend, escaped from his enemies by assuming various forms) is a specialised form of escape.

See **Flight.**

Psychosomatic behaviour

Psychosomatic behaviour (Greek psyche = soul and soma = body) is all behaviour directly motivated by physiological processes which, in turn, are triggered by psychological motives.

A dog which scratches itself without any clinical symptoms is said to show psychosomatic behaviour. The scratching is likely to be caused by psychological influences, such as fear-induced stress.

The concept of psychosomatic behaviour is of limited value from an ethological point of view, since it presupposes a clearly defined border between the psychological and the physiological. Ethology deals with both and with their common expression—behaviour.

Psychotherapy

Psychotherapy is the treatment of mental disorders by psychological means.

Psychotherapeutic programmes allow changes to a certain individual's motivation to perform a particular behaviour. When a dog is fearful of being alone at home, psychotherapy aims to substitute the fear connected with being left alone with, for example, the expectation of something good. When motivation is altered, subsequent behaviour is also changed.

PATHOLOGICAL BEHAVIOUR, UNDER-STIMULATION, STRESS, LONELINESS.

Psychotic behaviour

Psychotic (Greek psyche, or psukhé = soul and osis = condition) behaviour is a malfunction. There are two types of psychosis: (1) Reactive psychosis, triggered by environmental factors, and (2) organic psychosis, triggered by pathological malfunctions in the brain.

Whether animals can suffer from psychoses is unknown, but there are cases of pathological behaviour in dogs which show symptoms similar to those in humans.

PATHOLOGICAL BEHAVIOUR, NORMAL BEHAVIOUR.

Punishment

Punishment is the presentation of a negative reinforcement or the withdrawal of a positive reinforcement. Punishment must be distinguished from a negative reinforcement, which is something which when withdrawn increases the rate at which a certain behaviour is displayed.

A reinforcement leads to specific behaviour which can be foreseen. The effect of punishment can never be foreseen. Experiments have shown that punishment leads to fight, fear, helplessness, avoidance or flight.
    The effect of punishment is not lasting, even if it may be very strong and effective at the time. Punishment has therefore nothing to do with learning. It does not change the motivation to perform a certain behaviour. It only prevents it while it is present.

The effect of punishment is based on fear and it is therefore dangerous to use as a means of modifying behaviour. It may also lead to the unwanted conditioning of aversive stimuli, with far-reaching consequences.

LEARNING, LEARNING THEORIES, STIMULUS, REINFORCEMENT.

Rank order

Animals living in groups usually establish an order inside the group where each individual has a position in relation to the others. The purpose of a rank order, or hierarchy, is that it prevents fights and daily conflicts developing into serious combat. In a wolf pack or dog pack the leader, or alpha, is normally an elderly male. Often there is an elderly female as well, who shares overall leadership with the male, but is number one among all the females.

Dog owners often regard their 'pack' as comprising of the dog, or dogs, as well as human family members. The dog should regard itself as lower in rank than all human members and not regard children as lower-ranking puppies. Even if a human family functions as a pack in many respects, it's doubtful whether dogs regard the family as a real pack. Even more doubtful is whether a dog will act towards the family as it would towards other canine members of a pack. The bond between canine pack members is created, developed and maintained by the performance of daily survival strategies—finding prey, catching it, killing it and devouring it, to mention a few. It is when participating in these vital operations that the rank order is established, reversed or maintained. Pet owners do not participate in such activities and neither do their dogs. Generally, feeding procedures are routine and mundane. They do not demand any special skill besides opening the mouth, chewing and digesting—activities which have very little to do with deciding factors in rank ordering.

In order to achieve the alpha role in the family pack, the owner must therefore use artificial situations and exercises especially designed for this purpose.

RANK ORDERING, AGGRESSION, RITUALS, SOCIAL ANIMALS, LEADERSHIP.

Rank ordering

Rank ordering is the process of establishing a hierarchy. Rank ordering in wolves and dogs starts early. Cubs and pups try each other's strength constantly through play. Later, usually at the time of sexual maturity, hierarchy assumes a more serious role. Serious conflicts sometimes occur and a wolf maybe forced to leave the pack. The loser of a conflict may become a periphery wolf, living on the edges of the pack, always keeping a certain distance. If it comes too close it may be attacked and expelled once more. Eventually, this scapegoat may leave altogether. If it is lucky, it may find another lone wolf and wander around with it. Sometimes lone wolves do meet and succeed in finding a territory and forming a real pack, but these are exceptions to the rule.

Female alpha wolves tend to maintain their rank position longer than their male counterparts. If an alpha male loses his position and is forced to leave the pack the alpha female may choose to follow him, but she is just as likely to pair with the new alpha male and stay with her old pack.

The evolutionary purpose of rank ordering seems to be favouring of the fittest animals so they can pass on their genes to their progeny, the next generation.

RANK ORDER, AGGRESSION, SOCIAL ANIMALS.

The muzzle-nudge is an example of redirected behaviour—originating from self preservation it then become a ritualised pacifying gesture.

Redirected behaviour

A behaviour pattern can be said to be redirected when it has lost its original function but has kept a common element of it. The muzzle-nudge is an example of a redirected behaviour originating from the act of eliciting regurgitation. When the puppy is about five weeks old it begins butting at the parents' lips to make them regurgitate half-digested food. Later this muzzle-nudge is no longer elicited by hunger and the desire to cause regurgitation, but is a demand for acceptance and security.

MUZZLE-NUDGE, PAWING, FRIENDLINESS, PACIFYING BEHAVIOUR.

Reference system

An individual's reference system is made up of early experiences which are later used to judge situations. The reference system is built during imprinting and early socialisation.

Pathological behaviour may have its roots in a inappropriate reference system.

NEUROSIS, PATHOLOGICAL BEHAVIOUR, IMPRINTING.

Reflex

A reflex is a complex stimulus-response. A blow to the knee (stimulus) elicits a jump (response)—this is called the patella reflex and is unconditioned.

Some behaviour patterns in animals are reflex actions. In higher animals reflexes are only rudimentary patterns, usually concerned with self-preservation, such as breathing. Puppies suckle as a reflex whenever something is put into their mouths.

Reflexes may be conditioned (learned) or unconditioned (inborn). Classical conditioning can be used to teach dogs very simple patterns.

LEARNING, STIMULUS, RESPONSE, CONDITIONED BEHAVIOUR.

Regurgitation

Adult wolves regurgitate half-digested food for their cubs after returning to the den from a successful hunting excursion. The cubs lick them urgently around the lips to elicit regurgitation.

Domestic dogs sometimes regurgitate for their pups, but the majority have lost this parental skill through domestication and selective breeding.

Regurgitation, and the licking of the adults' lips, later becomes modified and develops into the muzzle-nudge behaviour which has a pacifying function.

MUZZLE-NUDGE, REDIRECTED BEHAVIOUR, MATERNAL BEHAVIOUR, PATERNAL BEHAVIOUR.

The cubs lick the adults urgently around the lips to elicit regurgitation.

Reinforcement

A reinforcement is everything which increases the rate at which a certain behaviour is displayed. There are two types of reinforcement. A positive reinforcement is everything that increases the rate at which a certain behaviour is displayed when presented. A negative reinforcement is everything which increases the rate at which a certain behaviour is displayed when withdrawn.

A reinforcement is unconditioned when it does not need previous learning, and conditioned when it requires learning. Giving a food treat to a dog to reinforce a certain response is an example of an unconditioned reinforcement. The expression 'good boy' as a reinforcement needs previous learning, as no dog is born with the knowledge of what 'good boy' means and the words themselves will not increase the rate at which any response is emitted. By presenting an unconditioned and a neutral reinforcement at the same time, the latter becomes conditioned in the same way as stimuli in conditioned reflexes.

Reinforcements are used to condition operant behaviour. Operant behaviour is behaviour influenced by the consequence of previous similar responses. An operant is everything that has an effect, something that acts upon something else.

Behaviour conditioned through reinforcement has to be maintained by presenting reinforcement on a random basis or it will undergo extinction. A response is said to be extinguished when its rate has returned to its initial low level because it was not followed by reinforcement.

There is often some confusion about the term reinforcement. Sometimes the term reward is used instead. Reward is usually defined as a pleasant thing that the individual experiences after performing a certain action. However, using this example, the use of a reward as a reinforcement is mistaken, as it has no learning effect at all. In usage by the classic school of operant conditioning, initiated by Skinner, reinforcement is a technical term for reward. However, British authors use the terms more freely.

STIMULUS, CONDITIONED BEHAVIOUR, LEARNING, LEARNING THEORIES, OPERANT CONDITIONING, REWARD, PUNISHMENT, REINFORCEMENT SCHEDULES.

Reinforcement schedules

The rate and regularity at which a reinforcement is presented is called a reinforcement schedule. A reinforcement schedule may be continuous (every desired response is reinforced), fixed interval (a reinforcement is given at set intervals provided the desired response occurs within that time), variable interval (the reinforcement is given at varying, unpredictable intervals), fixed ratio (a reinforcement is given for a fixed number of responses, however long this takes) and variable ratio (the reinforcement is given after a varying number of responses, so the number of responses required is unpredictable).

The type of reinforcement schedule used will affect the speed of response and the resistance to extinction of that behaviour. The most effective schedule of all in training is a variable ratio reinforcement schedule.

Reproduction

See **Sexual behaviour.**

Respiration

See **Breathing.**

Response

A response is everything elicited by a stimulus. A stimulus and a response produce a reflex.

REFLEX, STIMULUS, LEARNING, CONDITIONED BEHAVIOUR.

Resting behaviour

See **Behaviour.**

Reward

A reward is the pleasant experience that a dog receives after an action. A reward isn't necessarily something edible, even if this is often the case. Many dog owners reward their dog, in their opinion, by patting it on the head or chest.

There is some confusion about the concept of a reward. Some authors, notably British behaviourists, use rewards and positive reinforcements more or less interchangeably. The classic American behaviourists always use positive reinforcement when referring to operant conditioning or shaping. According to them, a reward, as commonly understood, has no learning effect.

REINFORCEMENT, LEARNING THEORIES.

Rituals

Rituals (Latin ritualis, ritus = habit, ceremony) are behaviour patterns which have lost their original function and have gained a meaning. The muzzle-nudge, for instance, is the ritualised stimulus for regurgitation.

Rituals are behaviour patterns which have lost their original function and have gained a meaning.Howling is the best-known ritual performed by the wolf. As well as a means of imparting information, the howl maintains the collective spirit of the pack.

All pack animals show ritualised behaviour. The more aggressive a species is, the more important rituals become. The ritualisation of aggression, for example, allows the peaceful solution of disputes. Rituals also serve to strengthen the bond between members of a pack. Rituals are behaviours with a very special meaning for the involved parties. Collective rituals serve to keep a group as a unit.

Howling is the best-known ritual performed by the wolf. As well as a means of imparting information, the howl maintains the collective spirit of the pack.

AGGRESSION, SOCIAL ANIMALS.

Dogs roll in smelly items. Has this behaviour any important goal, or is it only a question of taste?

Rolling in smelly items

There are three theories which might explain why dogs roll in smelly items.

A dog may be trying to camouflage its own odour. This is important when stalking prey. It is likely that prey animals find a strong smell, such as that of dead conspecifics, reassuring in some way, as it masks the smell of the predator. This theory is impossible to check.

Dogs may alternatively be trying to inform conspecifics that they have found an edible item. This hypothesis also proves impossible to verify.

Animals may also be trying to catch their conspecifics' attention. Smell may be used as a status symbol, but again this is impossible to prove. However, this explanation is likely to be closest to the truth as dogs which have rolled in something smelly do seem to draw the attention of other dogs. Where dogs are living in a pack, it may be that one temporarily enjoys the privileges of higher rank during the period where others investigate it, and enjoy the doubtful pleasure of its odour.

SCENT.

Sacrifice

See **Altruism.**

Scape-goat

The term scape-goat is used to designate a dog or wolf that has become unpopular in its pack and is subject to attacks from the others.

In a wolf pack, scape-goats may appear as a result of disputes over rank. Scape-goats live a miserable life on the periphery of the pack and sooner or later leave the pack forever. Scape-goats do not need to be unfit or particularly anti-social. Sometimes they may be caught in a fight at the wrong moment and become the subject of collective aggression. Winter conditions, which demand a lot from animals, or a female's oestrus, which increases aggression in a pack, mean that young wolves may suddenly become scape-goats. In domestic dog packs rehoming is usually the only option when a dog becomes a scape-goat.

RANK ORDERING, AGGRESSION.

Scent

Scent signals are very important for the dog because they have a very well-developed sense of smell. In relation to humans the dog has a much larger area of olfactory epithelium; the tissue in the nose which registers scent. This gives the dog the ability to detect extremely small quantities of scent and to distinguish smells accurately.

SCENT SIGNALS.

Scent signals

Dogs mark their territory with urine, probably spreading information about identity and rank. Females inform other dogs that they are about to come into season in this way. Scent marking with urine, and sometimes faeces, is mainly undertaken by males, but females also mark like this too, and very dominant females may mark

Dog owners should give their dogs—gund dogs as well as pet dogs—as many opportunities to search using their noses as possible. Searching and tracking exercises have proved to be an excellent remedy to cure under-stimulation and over-activity.

more frequently than others. Scent marking territory has almost no practical purpose for the pet dog, but it is indispensable for the wolf and other wild canids, especially in areas where packs have neighbouring territories.

A dominant, or a higher-ranking dog will always urinate over a lower-ranking dog's mark. In wolves it is only the alpha pair which marks.

Females mark using urine when they are in season and males may sometimes cover their mark with their own urine to emphasise a partnership. Some observations show that when a male wolf and a female wolf urinate together, they stay together, at least for the current season.

Secretions from the anal glands are probably important in scent marking and may even pass on other relevant information to the pack, but this is a matter which has not yet been fully studied.

Dog owners should give their dogs as many opportunities to search using their noses as possible. Searching and tracking exercises have proved to be an excellent remedy to cure under-stimulation and over-activity.

Even if the dog's sense of smell plays a very important role in their appreciation of the world, scent signals are probably not as important as visual signals in social behaviour and communication.

URINE, DEFECATION, MARKING, FACIAL EXPRESSIONS, BODY LANGUAGE, ANAL GLANDS, UNDER-STIMULATION.

Dogs mark their territory with urine, probably spreading information about identity and rank.

Season

See **Heat, Sexual behaviour, Oestrus**.

Selection

Selection is the process that changes the characteristics of a species or brings about new species. The individuals less adapted to their environment are eliminated before passing their unfit characteristics to offspring. The survivors are the fittest that pass their advantageous genes to their progeny.

Selection in domestic livestock is entirely dependant on human preferences. In the long run this may prove to be the way to create animals with some phenotypic characteristics that we like, but often it also results in the appearance of many unwanted characteristics, such as disease and problem behaviour. Organisms are more complicated than the human eye can perceive. When we select, we assume the role of nature and mistakes are unavoidable. All breeding should therefore be done with utmost care, and under the advice of knowledgeable people in the field.

Selective breeding

Selective breeding is the breeding we use in order to bring about certain characteristics that we like. It is through selective breeding that our dog breeds have come to look and behave the way they do, which reflects both our abilities and limitations.

SELECTION.

Self-preservation

Self-preservation is the drive, the energy, that keeps an individual alive. It is governed by physiological processes such as hunger, thirst and temperature regulation. Such processes trigger a number of behaviour patterns which serve to satisfy physiological needs.

Semiotic niche

An ecological niche is defined by all the factors that play a role in the survival of a certain species, e.g. types of food available, its predators or prey, tolerated weather. Two different species cannot experience a stable co-existence in exactly the same ecological niche.

A semiotic niche is defined by all the signals which prevail in the ecological niche of a certain species. A semiotic niche is a defined part of the global semiotic sphere, the sphere of all signals. In order to survive in the semiosphere a certain population needs to conquer a semiotic niche, to master a set of visual, acoustic, olfactory, tactile or chemical signs.

Man and dog live in different semiotic niches, but some understanding is possible as different species can co-exist in the same location provided they do not have exactly the same ecological niche. However, an opportunity for co-operation is the not the same as full understanding—a mistake many dog owners make. We will never be able to fully understand the dog's world, even if we are able to meet across our semiotic niches and establish positive co-operation. The human-dog bond is not unique; there are many examples of bonding between two species with benefits for both.

SIGN.

Sense organs

A sense organ is a part of an animal's body which contains receptors for specific stimuli. Sense cells, or receptors, transmit nervous impulses to specialised centres in the brain. This information is analysed and interpreted by the brain which in turn sends impulses to the different parts of the body, where action results.

The abilities and range of an animal's sense organs play a definitive role in behaviour. Sense organs receive information about the external world and it is through the combination of all information gathered by the different senses that we build our picture of the environment. A dog's representation of its environment must be very different to ours, since our senses differ so much. For example, the dog has a better sense of smell and hearing, while we are much more visually oriented. Animals of different species also have differently evolved centres of the brain for the interpretation of sense impressions.

The study of the senses is also important in understanding communication. All animals live in a world of signals and every species specialises in the specific use of a range of signals. We could say that every species conquers its own semiotic niche. Which semiotic niche a species occupies is a question of which senses it uses.

COMMUNICATION, HEARING, SIGHT, SIGN, SEMIOTIC NICHE

Separation

Dogs are social animals, and therefore react very strongly to being left alone. Canids are never alone when in a natural state and environment. Many problems occur for pet owners whose dogs never learn to cope with loneliness and separation. All dogs need to learn to be alone, but some find this easier than others.

Separation problems may manifest themselves through destructiveness, soiling and vocal distress. Some dogs show fear behaviour when left alone, while others show little more than dislike of isolation. Separation problems need to be solved by well-structured therapy programmes which must be carried out consistently for some period of time.

FEAR, SOCIAL ANIMALS.

Sexual behaviour

Sexual behaviour is all behaviour motivated by the drive of reproduction. Reproduction means passing on 50 per cent of one's genes. Sexual behaviour therefore plays its part in the evolution of species.

In dogs, sexual behaviour is elicited by the female's hormonal changes, called oestrus, which prepare her for reproduction. Pheromones cause the female to emit a characteristic smell which elicits the male's sexual behaviour. During oestrus male and female greet each other in a normal way, but appear to be a little more excited. Nose to nose contact takes place first, then nose to tail contact, or nose to genitals contact. The female quickly identifies the male's smell, but male dogs take their time while paying attention to a female in oestrus. Gradually, sexual behaviour may be elicited if the time is right. At this stage, the female usually jumps away and the male chases her. After much running and jumping, they may mate.

All behaviour which pre-empts mating is called courtship behaviour. It includes many aspects of play and infantile behaviour. Its function is probably to assure the female that the male will be a good father for her puppies. This is called sexual

Canine sexual behaviour includes a series of ritualised behaviour patterns.

selection. Females of most species are very selective about which males they mate with. They invest much energy in the process of conception, parturition and post-natal maternal behaviour and need to be sure that the genes their offspring inherit from the male are good and fit. Some courtship behaviour may go on for hours, and many females may only allow the male to mount them after spending the whole oestrus engaged in courtship behaviour.

Wolves develop preferences for each other and mating is not accidental. Normally, it is only the alpha wolves of both sexes that mate successfully and have progeny. This is to ensure the efforts of all pack members are concentrated on the survival of a few cubs instead of many. Since all pack members are probably related to the alpha male or female they have a genetic share in the cubs. In a sense, they are helping to reproduce their own genes, and this may well be the genetic explanation of altruism.

The dog's sexual behaviour is inborn, but experience helps to improve it! Young dogs usually need a few trials before a successful mating. Young females commonly refuse to be mounted, even when in full oestrus. Some breeders force such females to be mated by physically restraining them. However, it may be that a female is not ovulating at the designated time. Counting the number of days since the female first began to bleed is not a reliable method of judging this. A female that refuses to be mounted usually has her reasons, and this should be respected. Physiological or anatomical problems may mean she does not wish to accept a mate, or she may simply not be mature enough. Nature rarely makes mistakes in such an important issue as reproduction, and we should heed the warnings!

Sexual behaviour may also be used as an evasive or displacement behaviour. A dog which is in conflict may try to mount another to change the motivation of his own and the adversary's behaviour.

Dominance may also be shown by mounting. This is not motivated by the drive of reproduction.

MATING, HORMONES, PHEROMONE, SELECTION, OESTRUS, SEXUAL SELECTION.

Sexual drive

Sexual drive is the energy that motivates the individual to reproduce.

SEXUAL BEHAVIOUR, SEXUAL SELECTION, DRIVE.

Sexual organs

The sexual organs are the focus of much attention for wolves and dogs. In pack animals where males and females have their own separate rank order it is important to be able to identify a conspecific's sex. Inter-sexual aggression is rare. Females may show aggression towards pushy young males when they are close to coming into season, but a male is seldom aggressive towards a female.

It is likely that sniffing of the sexual organs gives dogs more information than just what sex the animal is. Age, rank and specific moods may also be read by means of olfactory analysis. A submissive dog may expose its genitals for another to sniff by using the twist movement— lifting its rear leg out to the side. If it is very submissive it may produce a few drops of urine to underline its submission. This behaviour has its origins in puppyhood where the mother used to over-turn the puppy and lick its belly and genitals. A submissive dog in this situation is therefore appealing to the other's nursery behaviour.

When a female is in oestrus sniffing of the genitals assumes a more important role. Indeed, the final act of mating is dependent on this behaviour. Males sniff and lick the female's genitals and experienced males may even be able to tell whether the female is ready for mating from this act.

Dog owners should let their dogs sniff each other, as this behaviour is part of their greeting ritual. Owners may provoke unnecessary fights by preventing dogs from greeting each other in this way.

GENITALS, GREETING, RITUALS, OESTRUS, COURTSHIP BEHAVIOUR, MATING.

Sexual selection

Sexual selection is the means by which certain secondary sexual characteristics have evolved. Females may chose their mating partners by selecting those that are better at courtship displays, better at nest building etc. From an evolutionary point of view, sexual selection is very important. Those chosen as mates are usually the fittest in some way and they will have a predominant influence on the next generation.

Female dogs tend to choose males according to criteria based on courtship behaviour.

SEXUAL BEHAVIOUR, SELECTION.

Shaping

Shaping was studied and described in detail by Burrhus Frederick Skinner (1904-1990) and is described in *The Behaviour of Organisms* (1938), *The Schedules of Reinforcement* (1957) and the *Analysis of Behaviour* (1961).

Shaping is a process of differentially reinforcing closer and closer approximations to a desired behaviour. In shaping any given behaviour we gradually change the criterion of what to reinforce. The desired behaviour is approached by successive approximation. For best results in shaping behaviour we should use conditioned reinforcers which should be presented in a close temporal relation to the response—which means as quickly as possible after the response.

Shaping is the learning method used when teaching complex skills. Complex skills must be shaped very gradually. As the criterion for differential reinforcement is shifted, successive approximations to the final behaviour are made. In gradually shifting the criteria of differential reinforcement we shape the desired behaviour through successive approximations.

Shaping is more than simple conditioning of a certain behaviour. Operant conditioning, for example, requires no differential reinforcement as the behaviour to be conditioned is attained in one attempt.

Shaping may be used to solve problems. For example, if a dog for some reason does not respond correctly to the signal 'down', we may use shaping. The first step consists of reinforcing the first movement downwards made by the dog, even if this is only a slight head movement. Secondly, we reinforce a more obvious downward movement, and only that. It is very important only to reinforce behaviour which successively approaches the goal we want to attain. Finally, we should only reinforce the dog's behaviour which consists of lying down with its belly touching the floor. Shaping requires time, patience, knowledge and skill from the teacher.

LEARNING THEORIES, OPERANT CONDITIONING, CONDITIONED BEHAVIOUR, REINFORCEMENT, REINFORCEMENT SCHEDULES.

Sight

Vision plays an important role in the overall communication of canids. The dog uses sight to detect another's facial expressions and body language.

Colour vision does not seem to be very well developed in the dog, but it is impossible to say whether dogs experience true Daltonism. The dog is certainly much better than us at focusing on moving objects, an important mechanism for a predatory animal.

Sign

A sign is a thing that means something to someone. A thing that means something to someone changes their behaviour.

A sign connects three elements: 1) The sign itself, 2) What the sign refers to, 3) The interpreter of the sign.

While humans generally use vocal signs to communicate, through language, dogs favour visual signals. This is the reason why canids have a highly evolved set of facial expressions and body gestures. The use of visual signals by humans for communication purposes differs radically from the dog's. Our signals are usually correlated with our abstract language while the dog's visual signals are of the simple type; „one signal —one action".

COMMUNICATION, SENSE ORGANS, SEMIOTIC NICHE, MISUNDERSTANDINGS BETWEEN PEOPLE AND DOGS.

Signal sensitivity

Signal sensitivity is a term used by Scandinavian behaviourists to describe the behaviour of dogs who interpret human facial and body language as if they were performed by dogs. For example, the human smile, consisting of opening the mouth and revealing the teeth, is interpreted as an aggressive threat.

Signal sensitivity is usually a product of insufficient socialisation of the puppy.

MISUNDERSTANDINGS BETWEEN PEOPLE AND DOGS.

Signals from human to dog

Since signals are everything that changes another's behaviour, dog owners must use signals carefully with their dogs. Often, the dog reacts to signals from its owner even though the owner did not intend to signal anything at all. At other times, we may believe we have taught the dog a certain signal, but we have not. For instance, many owners believe they have taught their dog to come to the signal 'here'. However, during the learning process they may sometimes have said 'here', while on other occasions they used 'come here' or 'hurry up, come here 'or 'come on now, here'. Such a tiny linguistic discrepancy is trivial for humans, but makes all the difference to the dog. The result is that the dog does not come when called and does not know the meaning of 'here'.

Dog owners are recommended to make a full list of all the signals they want to teach their dogs. Defining the meaning of each signal to indicate what behaviour they expect from the dog, plus the form of the signal, e.g. acoustic, visual, etc is extremely helpful.

Here is a list of some common signals to serve as an example.

Signal	Form	Meaning	Mistakes
Yes	Sound	Go on with what you're doing.	Come on.
			You may do it.
No	Sound	Stop now!	Don't do it.
			I said no.
Bongo (only if the dog is called Bongo)	Sound	Look at me.	Little-Bongo. Bongo-doggy.
Here Here	Sound Arms	Move directly and immediately towards me.	Come here. Will you come here now.
Down Down	Sound Hand	Belly on the ground now, where you are.	Down-down... I said down.
Sit Sit	Sound Hand	Bottom on the floor now, where you are.	Sit-sit-sit-sit. Come on sit. Sit down.

Sleep

Sleep is a necessity for many animals, allowing a state of reduced metabolic activity. During sleep there is a reduction in the electrical activity of the brain, which is recorded by an EEG (electroencephalogram) as low frequency, high amplitude waves, called slow-wave sleep. This state is interspersed by bouts of high frequency, low amplitude waves, associated with dreaming, often followed by rapid eye movement (REM). Interestingly, it is this REM period we truly call sleep.

Wolves sleep a lot when they are not hungry and are not providing food for cubs. During times when food is scarce they may wander for hours searching for prey, resting only occasionally.

Dogs often circle before settling down to sleep. This may well be to manoeuvre their spines into the right position before curling up to keep warm.

Modern society means that many dogs have little to do and spend too much time asleep. Most domestic dogs get food for free and do not need to hunt or provide for their progeny in any way. These dogs may become under-stimulated, resulting in behaviour which we find problematical. Dogs need to be activated.

UNDER-STIMULATION.

Slow movements

Slow movements show caution and therefore reveal either insecurity or submission. Fear may also be expressed by slow movements. In a tense situation where two dogs greet each other for the first time they both use slow movements in the preliminary phase.

However, hunting behaviour is an exception. Then, slow movements do not indicate social conflict or a rank problem. These movements reflect the concentration involved in stalking prey.

MOVEMENT, BODY LANGUAGE.

Smell

See **Scent, Scent signals.**

Some breeds of dog smile in a way which resembles a human smile. A smile should not be mistaken for a snarl.

Smile

Some breeds of dog smile in a way which resembles a human smile—the dog opens its mouth, draws back its lips and shows its teeth. A smile should not be mistaken for a snarl. The motivation behind a smile is pacification, while snarling is motivated by aggression.

Smiling behaviour in dogs is peculiar because it is a copy of the human smile, a phenocopy. It is also inherited and is usually seen as a family trait. The smile is only used by dogs towards humans, never to other dogs.

PACIFYING BEHAVIOUR, SNARL, PHENOCOPY.

When the dog snarls with lips curled forwards (left), it is aggressive and dominant. When it snarls with drawn back lips (right), it is aggressive and submissive. Dominance and submission are simultaneously emphasised by ears, eyes and tail.

Snarl

Snarling is the behaviour shown by a dog when it draws back its lips and shows its teeth, with or without a deep, characteristic sound. When the dog snarls with lips curled forwards, it means that the dog is aggressive and dominant. When it snarls with drawn back lips, the dog is aggressive and submissive. Dominance and submission are simultaneously emphasised by body signals using the ears, eyes and tail.

Snarling is always a display of aggression. When dog owners say their dogs snarl, but are fearful, they are confusing fear signals with submission or insecurity. In some pathologic cases, fear may be seen together with, or in close proximity to, snarling.

Smiling behaviour means friendliness, and should not be confused with snarling.

AGGRESSION, DOMINANCE, SUBMISSION, FEAR, PATHOLOGICAL BEHAVIOUR, CONTRADICTORY BEHAVIOUR, SMILE.

Snout

The word snout is usually used to designate the dog's nose and mouth area.

FACE, MARKING, FACIAL EXPRESSIONS, EYES, NOSE, MUZZLE-GRASP.

Social animals

Social animals are those which live in a socially organised group. The concept is difficult to define precisely, as a social organisation can consist of anything from the simple co-operation between a male and a female to the more complex organisation of an entire pack. Social organisations usually show a division of labour and a social order, which regulates activity.

Animals which live in a complex social group normally show a range of behaviour patterns motivated by dominance and submission, rather than aggression and fear.

SOCIAL BEHAVIOUR, RANK ORDER, PACK STRUCTURE, DOMINANCE, SUBMISSION.

Social behaviour

Social behaviour is all behaviour displayed during conspecific interaction. Social or pack animals have a large repertoire of social behaviour patterns.

PACK ANIMAL, COMMUNICATION, MATERNAL BEHAVIOUR, PATERNAL BEHAVIOUR, AGGRESSION, FEAR, DOMINANCE, SUBMISSION, RITUALS.

Sound signals

Dogs and wolves communicate by means of sound. Dogs are generally more noisy than wolves which is due to selective breeding by man, where we have favoured the noisiest animals. The ability to bark was probably one of the traits most favoured in the first dogs or wolves man encountered about 14,000 years ago.

Sound signals vary enormously. The following table groups signals according to motivation, i.e. aggression, fear, dominance, submission and other social contexts.

HOWL, BARKING.

Aggression	
Growl 1	deep and low in tone, coming from the chest.
Snarl 1	a growl which is not so deep or low.
Bark 1	a quick, repeated bark.
Bark 2	a quick, repeated bark, more varied in tone than bark 1, with snarling, most often used by lower ranking dogs.
Fear	
Whine 1	a long whine, eventually rising in pitch.
Howl 1	a single high howl.
Bark 3	repeated, high-pitched bark, bordering on a whine.
Dominance/superiority	
Snarl 2	as snarl 1, but softened.
Growl 2	as growl 1, but short.
Submission/inferiority	
Whine 2	a quick scream, high in pitch.
Whimper	a sort of whine only used by puppies.
Other social contexts	
Whine 3	a short repeated whine, used with allelomimetic effect—either an invitation to play or asking for contact.
Bark 4	a light, high-pitched bark—an invitation to interact.
Woof	a quick sound which is full of air—used as 'watch-out', an alarm.
Bark 5	very like bark 1, it is most often used to warn other pack members, including owners, of the presence of strangers in the territory.
Whine 4	like whine 1, but used by puppies when they call for help.
Howl 2	the wolf howl - used when lonely or during pack rituals.

Staring

Staring is the dog and the wolf's most commonly used sign of dominance. The dominant individual stares at its adversary and usually forces it to show submissive behaviour or to flee. When a dog stares intensely at another it shows deep concentration. The animal's body is stiff and it shows other signs of dominance. Gradually,

Staring is the dog and the wolf's most commonly used sign of dominance. When a dog stares intensely at another it shows deep concentration.

as the opponent shows increasing submission the staring becomes less intense and finally the dominant dog continues on its path. The submissive dog may show active submission by licking the dominant one's mouth, or it may lie down in a demonstration of passive submission.

Staring can be successfully used by dog owners towards their dogs. Dogs react submissively or show pacifying gestures to this behaviour. However, care should be taken when staring at unknown dogs. Staring can be regarded as a threat and may elicit an attack. Fearful dogs may also respond badly to being stared at, as their fear is likely to increase.

FACIAL EXPRESSIONS, DOMINANCE, SUBMISSION, THREAT, FEAR, PACIFYING BEHAVIOUR.

Stimulus

A stimulus is everything that elicits a response. A stimulus and a response define a reflex. Stimuli may be unconditioned, when they do not require previous learning, or conditioned, when they have required learning.

RESPONSE, REFLEX, LEARNING THEORIES, CONDITIONED BEHAVIOUR.

Stimulus Object

A stimulus object is everything that elicits a stimulus. It must be distinguished from the stimulus, which elicits a response.

STIMULUS, CLASSICAL CONDITIONING.

Stop

The stop is the area of the dog's face where the muzzle meets the forehead.

Stress

Stress is a physiological reaction to external factors which prepares an animal for dealing with extreme situations. When a dog senses danger, stress prepares it for fight or flight. Equally, the perception of prey stresses the predator so that it concentrates its energy, ready for the moment of chase. Prey animals also need a well-functioning stress mechanism to prepare for escape.

Stress is a healthy reaction from the organism and serves self-preservation. However, it can cause pathologic responses, e.g. disease or abnormal behaviour, if the organism remains under stress for too long or too often.

Learning is a stressful process, as an individual must deal with new impulses. Learning represents a confrontation with the unknown. We should therefore aim at training sessions which are as quiet and stress-free as possible in order not to increase stress further to a point where learning is impossible and fear or avoidance behaviour result.

LEARNING, PHYSIOLOGY.

Active submission (left) and passive submission (right).

Submission

The concept of submission is integral to understanding social behaviour. This concept is intimately related to fear, as dominance is to aggression. The four great motivational factors, i.e. fear, submission, aggression and dominance, determine the behaviour displayed during social interactions. For a detailed explanation of the concept of submission see under *Dominance*.

Submission may also be called inferiority or insecurity. From a behavioural point of view, submission, inferiority or insecurity are shown in canids by the following behaviour patterns:
- lowered ears, possibly totally flattened
- drawn back lips, without showing the teeth
- small, elongated eyes, blinking
- flattened forehead
- cringing, fawning
- lowered tail, sometimes totally between the legs.

There are two main ways that submissive behaviour is shown: 1) active submission, where the dog actively tries to pacify its adversary, for example, muzzle-nudging, and (2) passive submission, when the dogs lies down passively, belly up, and lets the opponent sniff and eventually lick it. Strictly speaking, there is a third variation which the author calls 'semi-active submission', which consists of passive submission where the dog or wolf raises the head and muzzle-nudges in the air without contact with the opponent.

The insecure dog behaves submissively with half closed eyes, drawn back ears, retracted lips and lowered tail.

Submission is learned around the fifth week of the puppy's life. The mother, and eventually the father, teach the puppy these mechanisms. In the wild, most pack members also participate in the socialisation of youngsters and teach them what we could call the A.B.C. of canine language.

DOMINANCE, FEAR, AGGRESSION, MATERNAL BEHAVIOUR, RANK OR-DER, PATERNAL BEHAVIOUR, PACK ANIMAL, SELECTION.

Superiority

See **Dominance.**

Survival

Survival is the most important principle in nature. Organisms have assumed forms and functions with the sole purpose of surviving as long as possible to reproduce, so that some of their genes are spread in the universal gene pool.

In nature, life and death are closely connected. Life is the only thing which can be said to be objectively good in itself. The ethics of nature are simple. Everything that favours life and its conditions is good—everything that threatens life or inhibits it is bad. This system governs all forms of life from microscopic single-celled organisms, to complicated and highly-developed animals.

SELECTION.

Tail

Dog breeds have tails of many different shapes and sizes which are due to mutations of the original wolf tail and selective breeding. The tail is an extension of the spinal column and acts as a stabiliser when the dog moves, especially when it runs and needs to execute tight turns. This stabilising influence is very important in maintaining the animal's balance.

The tail is also used to signal to other dogs and to humans.

TAIL LANGUAGE, TAIL DOCKING, BODY LANGUAGE.

See illustrations pages 240-241.

A Boxer with docked tail. In some countries it is now forbidden to dock tails and crop ears—a victory for Nature!

Tail docking

Tail docking is the term for surgery when a part or the whole of the tail is removed. There is no satisfactory reason for tail docking.

Dogs with docked tails find it more difficult to maintain balance under speed and they are obviously inhibited in their tail expression. A German Shepherd or a Siberian Husky with a full-length tail finds it easier to perform tight turns at high speed than, for example, breeds which are traditionally docked, such as the Rottweiler or Old English Sheepdog, which appear clumsy. Dogs which have docked tails, such as the Cocker Spaniel, usually exaggerate tail wagging to try to compensate for their missing tails.

In many countries tail docking is now forbidden by law and there is no doubt it is only a question of time before all countries in the world adhere to the principle of respecting the anatomy with which dogs are born.

TAIL LANGUAGE, MOVEMENT.

Tail language

Dogs use their tails to emphasise signals expressed by facial and body postures, or vocally.

High tail carriage is usually associated with dominance and a low tail carriage with submission. It is important to recognise that the tail is more likely to follow dominance and submission than aggression and fear. For example, a dog showing aggression and submission at the same time shows a low tail carriage.

Wagging doesn't only mean friendliness. A tail which is carried high, combined with a slight wag, emphasises the dog's dominance. A slight wagging in a lower position may be a preparation for attack. Puppies and young dogs may wag with their tails tucked between their legs, sometimes even when lying on their backs, to signal their unconditional submission. Such wagging probably spreads their scent, appealing to the adults' parental feelings and pacifying them. During attack, the tail is lowered to a horizontal position in the dominant dog.

The language of the tail is usually clear. It is likely that misunderstandings can occur between dogs with docked or deformed tails, especially at a distance.

TAIL DOCKING, BODY LANGUAGE.

Tails have various forms and shapes—the result of mutations and selections. Some tails are not purposeful for communication.

Tail language — The normal tail position at the top. Left from top to bottom there is an increase in dominance. Right from top to bottom there is an increase in submission. The dog's facial and bodily expression support the message of the tail. Notice ears, head position and legs.

Taste

We do not know much about the dog's sense of taste. It doesn't seem to be very well evolved in comparison to ours, but such a 'question of taste' is impossible to prove!

It has been observed that wolves develop preferences towards certain prey and when given the choice they pick one rather than another. Experiments with dogs have shown that many are quite conservative regarding their favourite foods. When given a new palatable food they will probably change over for a while, but tend to come back to the old favourite food after a short time. The best way to choose food for your dog in our modern society may be after consultation with your veterinary surgeon.

JACOBSON'S ORGAN.

Teat-nudge

The teat-nudge is the original form of the muzzle-nudge, which develops later. The puppy nudges its mother's teats immediately after birth, to stimulate the production of milk.

New-born puppies are able to find their mother's teats and perform this nudging without prior experience. However, there is no doubt that the ability to perform this behaviour improves with experience during the first few days after birth.

MUZZLE-NUDGE, NEONATAL BEHAVIOUR, REDIRECTED BEHAVIOUR.

Teeth

Teeth are often used in communication through snarling, which is a display of aggression. Showing the teeth thus becomes a sign of aggression. The submissive dog keeps its teeth hidden.

Pups and cubs may sometimes bite adults during excited greetings, although this is always gentle.

AGGRESSION, SNARL, FACIAL EXPRESSIONS.

Territorial behaviour

Pack animals have territories that they defend against rival packs. The territory is marked with the help of all available signals. Canids usually scent mark their territory. Pack members are likely to show more aggression the closer an adversary gets to the centre of the territory. Bloody battles between rival wolf packs have been known to occur where one pack has trespassed over the other's boundary. Some of these encounters end in death.

Our dogs are also likely to show an increase in aggressive behaviour when another dog enters their territory, either in their home or garden. A dog which encounters a furious attack from another on its home territory, may be well received and accepted when the same two dogs meet on neutral ground. This is the reason why a newly acquired dog should be introduced to an established dog in a neutral place, prior to taking it home.

TERRITORY, PACK ANIMAL, AGGRESSION.

Territory

The territory is the geographic place used by an animal or a pack to survive. Here, they find food, shelter and raise their offspring. Territories are marked out by signs such as faeces, urine and scratching. A wolf pack territory is defended by all members, especially during the mating season and when there are cubs to be protected.

Our dogs usually regard their home and garden as their territory. However, some dogs have other ideas about the boundaries of their territory or their overall rank in the neighbourhood, and readily scent mark all over the local area. Such excessive scent marking is never observed in nature and is only tolerated in our society because dogs have lost their natural territories and true territorial sense. The instinct to scent mark remains, but is now little more than an opportunity for most dogs to emphasise their presence and dominance.

TERRITORIAL BEHAVIOUR, MARKING, SCENT SIGNALS.

Threat

A threat is a signal of aggression. Normally, a dog will threaten another before attacking. It shows clear signs of aggression and dominance, or submission. To defuse a threat dogs use pacifying behaviour. Dogs rarely continue to attack an adversary after threatening it, as long as it shows clear pacifying behaviour, submission or retreat.

When a wolf or a dog threatens another with an open-mouthed gape it demonstrates its readiness for attack. Threats are common during rank-related skirmishes, but most end without serious consequences. Uninhibited attacks are only seen in serious rank disputes where the aggressor intends to expel its opponent from the pack. Here, compromise by submission is not an option.

AGGRESSION, DOMINANCE, SUBMISSION, RANK ORDER.

Throat

The throat is the front part of the neck.

See **Neck** and **Neck positions**.

Thrusting

Thrusting is the movement which male dogs perform while mating. Thrusting doesn't need to be sexually motivated. Dominant dogs may use this behaviour towards submissive dogs to show their dominance. Even if this is more usually seen among males, dominant females may also use it to display their rank. Neutered females may be more liable to mount than unneutered ones.

Thrusting may also be a displacement activity. Occasionally, a dog may try to turn its fear into sexual motivation, either by presenting its rear end to its opponent, or by mounting it.

SEXUAL BEHAVIOUR, PENIS, REDIRECTED BEHAVIOUR.

Tie

Two bodies called the corpus cavernosus lie on both sides of the dog's penis. During copulation these bodies fill with blood, enlarging to such an extent that it is impossible for male and female to separate for between five and 30 minutes. This is called the tie. Some dogs remain locked in the tie even longer.

In situations of stress the corpus cavernosus may sometimes enlarge. This is especially easy to see in short-haired dogs like the Dobermann.

Some dogs remain locked in the tie for 30 minutes or even longer.

Twist movement

Twist behaviour is the movement shown by a wolf or a dog when it twists one hind leg out to the side. The purpose of this behaviour is to pacify an opponent. Its origins are found in maternal behaviour when the female overturns the puppy by pressing her nose against its groin, forcing one hind leg to the side. This appears to be a rather unpleasant experience for puppies to start with, but rapidly becomes pleasurable once they are overturned and their mother licks their fat bellies. Later on, the puppies perform a twist movement independently. This is then a redirected behaviour, aimed at pacifying their mother.

The term *twist movement* originates from the author's memories of his misspent youth, when the famous sixties dance, the Twist, was popular. The Twist featured a characteristic step, where the dancer's legs made a movement reminiscent of the puppy's pacifying behaviour.

INFANTILE BEHAVIOUR, MATERNAL BEHAVIOUR, SUBMISSION.

Many years before John, Paul, George and Ringo sang 'Twist And Shout,' wolves and dogs twisted at they pleased or found necessary. Twist behaviour is the movement shown by a wolf or a dog when it twists one hind leg out to the side. The purpose of this behaviour is to pacify an opponent.

Under-stimulation

We say that a dog is under-stimulated when it is given insufficient opportunity to use and develop its inborn abilities and satisfy its needs.

Under-stimulation is the most common cause for the so-called problem dog. The dog may react by barking excessively, or by being excessively pushy or friendly during greeting ceremonies. Aggression may also be a result of under-stimulation.

The cure for under-stimulation is to activate the dog through artificial exercises. The dog's natural abilities can be developed and utilised through tracking, searching, body control exercises and problem solving.

NORMAL BEHAVIOUR, PATHOLOGICAL BEHAVIOUR.

Unselfishness

See **Altruism.**

Urine

Urine is the fluid medium excreted by animals to remove metabolic waste products from the system. In the dog, urine is produced by the kidneys, stored in the bladder and excreted through the urethra. In males it passes through the penis.

Urine is used by canids to scent mark their territory. Males normally scent mark posts in their territory, especially around borders. Male and female may scent mark together during the mating season to emphasise their union.

Males begin to lift their legs to urinate when approaching sexual maturity. This varies greatly from breed to breed. Most male dogs begin to lift their legs from seven to 14 months of age. Males that lift their legs earlier normally develop into very dominant individuals. Females occasionally scent mark as well, and they too may lift their legs to do so. Some may cock their leg in the same way as males, others even manage to lift both legs off the ground in an amazing acrobatic display.

Females in heat scent mark more frequently than usual, to inform males of their hormonal status.

Some dogs do not dare to urinate outside their home territory. Usually these dogs are fearful and insecure and do not wish to leave their mark on foreign soil.

SCENT SIGNALS, TERRITORIAL BEHAVIOUR.

Vision

See **Sight.**

Visual communication

Visual communication encompasses all the signs apprehended by the eye which change the receiver's behaviour. Dogs are very oriented towards visual communication.

FACIAL EXPRESSIONS, BODY LANGUAGE.

The term biotonus—*vitality —refers to the puppy's ability to find warmth and the mother's teats.*

Vitality

Vitality is the puppy's life energy. Puppies are genetically programmed to act in certain ways immediately after birth. The most important resources for a puppy are warmth and food. The term *biotonus*—vitality —refers to the puppy's ability to find warmth and the mother's teats. If a puppy happens to be too far away from the mother it will try to locate her and come back with typical pendulum movements of the head. It will crawl in a spiral to find her. The puppy has an inborn picture of the nipples, made up of a combination of smell and touch impressions. The pup who isn't able to find its way back to the mother, or find the teats by itself, is said to have a bad biotonus—low vitality. These puppies would die without human intervention.

NEONATAL BEHAVIOUR.

Vocal language

See **Sound signals, Communication, Language.**

Wagging

Tail wagging is normally assumed to show happiness in the dog. However, there are exceptions, and it is therefore more accurate to say that tail wagging emphasises other signals.

The friendly dog wags its tail in a more or less horizontal position, to draw attention to itself. The dominant dog wags its tail slowly in an upright position, signalling its rank. A dog showing active submission wags its tail in a low carriage, while simultaneously showing pacifying behaviour through other body signals. Puppies and young dogs which lie down to show passive submission may pass a few drops of urine and then wag their tails to spread the odour. This assures the opponent that the submissive animal poses no threat.

Light wagging in a low position may indicate uncertainty.

Dogs with docked tails, a practice forbidden in Scandinavia, and dogs whose tails constantly stand upright, such as terriers, cannot signal to each other in the same way. Dogs with docked tails often wag their entire rear ends. Terriers may sometimes be misunderstood, and a totally friendly dog may appear to be dominant, simply by its tail carriage.

TAIL, TAIL LANGUAGE.

Whine

Whining is an acoustic method of communication. It is a long high-pitched sound, normally associated with distress, submission, insecurity or fear.

Some dogs may learn to whine constantly for attention. The origins of the problem may be related to distress, pain or stress in a situation where the owner was present. If owners do not attempt to stop it, whining becomes a fixed pattern. This can be cured by means of appropriate behavioural programmes.

It is normal for puppies to whine when in distress, e.g. when left alone, or frustrated by the inability to solve a certain problem.

SOUND SIGNALS.

Whiskers

Whiskers are the thick hairs on each side of the muzzle. They function as a sensory organ. We do not know exactly how important whiskers are for the dog, but we are justified in assuming that they have a significant role when we compare their use in other animals.

If this is true, dog owners should be discouraged from trimming their dog's whiskers for so-called aesthetic reasons.

SENSE ORGANS.

Xenophobia—some dogs have to learn how to greet strangers.

Xenophobia

Xenophobia (Greek ksenos = living being, and phobia = fear) is a fear of strangers. All dogs have inborn xenophobia which protects them. All strangers or unknown experiences are regarded with suspicion until the dog is assured of its peaceful intentions.

It is normal for dogs to greet strangers before they become outwardly friendly. Some breeds demand more acquaintance before intimacy than others. However, it is not normal for any breed to show extreme xenophobia to the point of displaying fear of strangers. We must breed dogs so that they socialise easily and happily—the fundamental basis behind the evolution of the domestic dog, *Canis lupus familiaris*.

PACK ANIMAL.

Yawn

The dog's yawn is very similar to ours. It is often accompanied by the same characteristic sound. Yawning is popularly associated with tiredness or boredom. In reality, it can be an expression of embarrassment, insecurity, excitement and relief. Some humans yawn when they are in love, which can be embarrassing if it is mistaken for boredom!

Dogs certainly yawn when they are tired, but more usually they display this behaviour to pacify an opponent. Yawning is a friendly and contagious behaviour trait. For example, a male dog may yawn if the female snarls at him during the mating ceremony. The dominant dog yawns to show friendliness to the submissive, and vice versa. Dogs yawn to show us that they are friendly and to appease us. They use the yawn as a displacement activity. A typical situation where we can observe a dog yawn is when the owner scolds it. Another is when training the so-called 'stay', where the behaviour of the owner causes the dog to feel insecure. A yawn is likely to follow, together with licking and muzzle-nudging. When the owner changes behaviour, for instance, by using a more friendly voice or body posture, the dog's pacifying behaviour disappears.

PACIFYING BEHAVIOUR, FRIENDLINESS, MUZZLE-NUDGE, LICKING, DISPLACEMENT ACTIVITY.

Zoology

Zoology is the science of studying animals, their anatomy, physiology, morphology, genetics, ecology, evolution and behaviour. Ethology is a specialised field of zoology.

ETHOLOGY, ECOLOGY, CYNOLOGY.

Bibliography

Abrantes, R., Hallgren, A. (1982) - On the Testing of Behavioural Traits.

Abrantes, R.A., (1982) - Indlæringspsykologi.

Abrantes, R.A., (1983) - Inquiry into the Effectiveness of Human-Dog Communication (IEMT, Wien).

Abrantes, R.A., (1984) - Moderen, om hundemoderens rolle i hvalpenes udvikling (Jagthunden).

Abrantes, R.A., (1984) - De fædreløse, om hundefaderens rolle i hvalpenes udvikling (Jagthunden).

Abrantes, R.A., (1986) - Hunden, vor ven - psykologi fremfor magt.

Abrantes, R.A., (1986) - Hunden er aggressiv.

Abrantes, R.A., (1986) - Hunden er angst.

Abrantes, R.A., (1986) - Hunden er alene hjemme.

Abrantes, R.A., (1986) - Hundens ankomst til hjemmet.

Abrantes, R.A., (1986) - Hund og barn.

Abrantes, R.A., (1986) - The Expression of Emotions in Man and Canid (Waltham Symposium, Cambridge University).

Abrantes, R.A., (1987) - Hundesprog.

Abrantes, R.A., (1993) - The Develpoment of Social Behaviour. (in *The Behaviour of Dogs and Cats*, by members of the APBC).

Abrantes, R., (1994) - Hunden—ulven ved din side.

Abrantes, R.A., (1994) - The Art and Science of Communication (in Transcript of Waltham APBC Symposiun 1994).

Abrantes, R.A., (1997) - The Evolution Of Canine Social Behaviour.

Abrantes, R.A., (1997) - How do I know what I know?—An Introduction To Epistemology.

Alderton, D., (1992) - You and Your Pet Bird.

Allan, R. & C., (1988) - German Shepherd Dogs.

Althaus, T., (1986) - Development of the Harmonic Relationship Between Owner and Dog.

Andresen, E., (1976) - Det genetiske grundlag for husdyravl.

Appleby, D., (1990) - The Good Behaviour Guide.

Appleby, D., (1992) - How To Have A Happy Puppy

Aristoteles - Historia Animalum (overs. Peck, A.L., 1979).

Ayala, F.J., Kiger, J.A., (1980) - Modern Genetics.

Ayer, A.J., (1972) - Probability and Evidence.

Bailey, G., (1992) - Leading the Pack - How to control the wild side of your dog.

Beaver B., (1994) The Veterinarian's Encyclopedia of Animal Behavior.
Bjerre, J., (1980) - Sirius - Danmarks slædepatrulje i Nordøstgrønland.
Boone, J.A., (1954) - Kinship with all Animals.
Borchelt, P.L., (1982) - Behavior Development of the Puppy in the Home Environment.
Borchelt, P.L., (1982) - Development of Behavior of the Dog during Maturity.
Bolvig, N., (1982) - Primaternes verden.
Borger, R & Seaborne, A.E.M., (1966) - The Psychology Of Learning.
Burger, I., (1993) - The Watham Book Of Companion Animal Nutrition.

Case, L. et al., (1994) - Companion Animal Management.
Case, L. et al., (1995) - Canine And Feline Nutrition.
Chomsky, N., (1972) - Language and Mind.
Christensen, I.C., (1975) - Beagle.
Christensen, I.C., (1976) - Basset Hound.
Christiansen, F.W & Rothausen, B., (1983) - Behaviour Patterns Inside and Around the Den of a Captive Wolf Pack.
Clothier, S., (1996) - The Seven C's - Training & Relationships.
Cox, T., (1978) - Stress.
Cullberg, I., (1984) - Dynamisk Psykiatri.

Damasio, A.R., (1994) - Descarte's Error.
Darwin, C., (1859) - The Origin of Species.
Darwin, C., (1872) - The Expression of the Emotions in Man and Animals.
Darwin, C., (1978) - The Voyage of Charles Darwin, edited by C. Ralling.
Darwin, C., (1982) - Darwin og hans rejse med Beagle.
Dawkins, R., (1976) - The Selfish Gene.
Dawkins, R., (1982) - The extended phenotype.
Dawkins, R., (1986) - The Blind Watchmaker.
Dawkins, M.S., (1986) - Unravelling Animal Behaviour.
De Waal, F., (1982) - Chimpanzee Politics - Power and Sex Among Apes.
Dickinson, A., (1980) - Contemporary Animal Learning Theory.
Downer, J., (1988) - Supersense - Perception in The Animal World.
Dunbar, I., (1979) - Dog Behavior - Why Dogs Do What They Do.
Dunbar, I., (1991) - How to Teach a New Dog Old Tricks.
Dunbar, I., (1995) - The New Puppydog.
Dunbar, I., (1996) - Good Little Dog Book.
Dunbar, I., Bohnenkamp., (1985) - Behaviour Boolets.
Düring, K., (1975) - Breton.

Edney, A.T.B., (1982) - Dog And Cat Nutrition.
Eibl-Eibesfeldt, I., - (1970) -Kærlighed og had.
Eibl-Eibesfeldt, I., - (1975) - Det præprogrammerede menneske.
Eklund, B., (1981) - Pälsvård, trimning och klippning.

Eklund, B., (1981) - Parning och valpning.

Feign, L., (1992) - How Animals Do It.
Fisher, J., (1990) - Think Dog.
Fisher, J., (1991) - Why Does My Dog...?
Fisher, J., (1992) - Dogwise - The Natural Way to Train Your Dog.
Fisher, J., (1993) - Reinforcement Training for Dogs.
Fogle, B., (1983) - Pets and their People.
Fogle, B., (1988) - Paws Across London.
Fogle, B., (1990) - The Dog's Mind.
Fox, M.W., (1966) - Behavioural Effects of Differential Early Experience in the Dog.
Fox, M.W., (1967) - Development of the Delayed Response in the Dog.
Fox, M.W., (1968) - Abnormal Behavior in Animals.
Fox, M.W., (1968) - Aggression Its Adaptive and Maladaptive Significance in Man and Animals.
Fox. M.W., (1971) - Overview and Critique of Stages and Periods in Canine Development.
Fox, M.W., (1971) - Towards a Comparative Psychopathology.
Fox, M.W., (1971) - Behaviour of Wolfes, Dogs and Related Canids.
Fox, M.W., (1972) - Socio-Ecological Implications of individual Differences in Wolf Litters: A Developmental and Evolutionary Perspective.
Fox, M.W., (1972) - The Social Significance of Genital Licking in the Wolf, Canis Lupus.
Fox, M.W., (1972) - Social Dynamics of Three Captive Wolf Packs.
Fox, M.W., (1973) - Physiological and Biochemical Correlates of Indivedual Differences in Behaviour of the Wolf.
Fox, M.W., (1974) - Understanding Your Dog.
Fox, M.W., (1974) - Understanding Your Cat.
Fox, M.W., (1975) - The Wild Canids.
Fox, M.W., (1977) - What Is Your Dog Saying.
Fox, M.W., (1978) - Man, Wolf and Dog.
Fox, M.W., (1980) - The soul of the Wolf.
Fox, M.W., (1990) - Superdog.
Fraser, J & Ammen, A., (1991) - Dual Ring Dog.
Freeman, R., (1972) - Classification of the Animal Kingdom.
Fromm, E., (1974) - The Anatomy of Human Destructiveness.
Fält, L., (1976) - Förstå din hund.
Fält, L., (1982) - Inheritance of Behaviour in the Dog.

Geppert, J. & Visalberghi - The Return of the Wolf (video).
Goodall, J., (1990) - Animal World, Chimps.
Goodwin, B., (1984) - How The Leopard Changed It's Spots.
Grosemans, D. (1991) - Omgaan Met Hond & Kat.

Gubernick, D.J. & Klopfer, P.H., (1981) - Parental Care in Mammals.
Gustafson, M., (1983) - Hundliv, om psykisk hälsa i mänsklig miljö.
Gustafson, M., (1990) - Bare en hund.

Hallgren, A., (1971) - Problemhundar och hundproblem.
Hallgren, A., (1974) - Få en glad og lydig hund.
Hallgren, A., (1974) - Lyckliga lydiga hundar.
Hallgren, A., (1978) - Hund och människa.
Hallgren, A., (1981) - Arga Hundar.
Hallgren, A., (1984) - En Jycke betyder så mycke!
Hallgren, A., (1984) - Hundens gyllene regler.
Hallgren, A., (1984) - Idel, ädel, avel.
Hallgren, A., (1986) - Lexikon i hundespråk.
Hallgren, A., (1988) - Tikens dominans.
Halliday, T.R., Slater, P.J.B., (1983) - Causes and Effects.
Halliday, T.R., Slater, P.J.B., (1983) - Communication.
Halliday, T.R., Slater, P.J.B., (1983) - Genes, Developments and Learning.
Hansen, L., (1989) - Agility - også for din hund.
Hart, B.L., (1980) - Canine Behavior.
Hart, B.L., (1988) - The Perfect Puppy.
Hartmann-Kent, S., (1990) - Your Dog & Your Baby.
Hess, E.H., (1973) - Imprinting.
Hjelmer Jørgensen, H., (1982) - Dominanshieraki og nonverbal kommunikation.
Hjelmer Jørgensen, H., (1982) - Grønlandsk slædehund og ulv.
Hoffmeyer, J., (1993) - En snegl på vejen.
Holland, J.G., Skinner, B.F., (1961) - The Analysis of Behavior.
Houpt, K. A., (1991) - Domestic Animal Behaviour.
Hutt, F.B., (1979) - Genetics for Dog Breeders.

James, W., (1983) - The Principles of Psychology.
Joby, R., Jemmett, J.E., Miller, A.S.H., (1984) - The control of undesirable behaviour in male dogs using megestrol acetate.
Johnston, B., (1990) - The Skilful Mind Of The Guide Dog.
Johansen, A., (1971) - Jagthundens dressur.
Jones, S., (1993) - The Lagunage of the Genes.
Jäverud, S., (1981) - Din hund.

Kendell, R.E. & Zealley, A.K., (1973) - Companion to Psychiatric Studies.
Krushinskii, L.V., (1960) - Animal Behavior—its normal and abnormal Development.
Kruuk, H., (1972) - The Spottes Hyena—A Study of Predation and Social Behavior.

Larsen, H., (1947) - Politihundedressur.
Leakey, R. E., (1981) - The Making of Mankind.

Leakey, R.E., (1994) - The Origin Of Humankind.

Little, C.C., (1957) - The Inheritance of Coat Color in Dogs.

Lloyd, H.S., (1983) - Cocker Spaniels

Lopez, B., (1978) - Of Wolves And Men.

Lorenz, K., (1963) - Das sogenannte Böse.

Lorenz, K., (1965) - Evolution and Modification of Behavior.

Lorenz, K., (1969) - På talefod med dyrene.

Lorenz, K., (1973) - Die Rückseite des Spiegels.

Lorenz, K., (1974), - Hundeliv.

Lorenz, K., (1981) - The Foundations of Ethology.

Lorenz, K., (1983) - Nedbrydningen af det menneskelige.

Ludwig, A.M., (1986) - Principles of Clinical Psychiatry.

McConell, P.B., (1996) - Leader Of The Pack.

McClearn, G.E. & DeFries, J.C., (1973) - Introduction to Behavioral Genetics.

McFarland, D., (1981) - The Oxford Companion to Animal Behaviour.

Mech, D., (1970) - The Wolf.

Mech, D., (1988) - The Arctic Wolf: Living with the Pack.

Morris, D., (1967) - The Naked Ape.

Morris, D., (1994) - The Human Animal.

Mortensen, A., (1983) - Bogen om boxeren.

Mugford, R.A., (1982) - Behaviour Problems in the Dog.

Mugford, R.A., (1982) - Methods Used to Describe the Normal and Abnormal Behaviour of the Dog and Cat.

Mugford, R.A., (1992) - Dog Training The Mugford Way - Never Say No!

Mugford, R. A., - The Halti Way of Dog Training.

Mugford, R.A. & Gupta, A.S., (1984) - Genetics and Behavioural Problems in Dogs.

Møller, G., (1974) - Dyrenes adfærd.

Neville, P., (1991) - Do Dogs Need Shrinks?

Nørlund, A.P., (1949) Spaniels.

Nørlund, A.P., (1969) Cocker og springer spaniel.

O'Farrell, V., (1989) - Problem Dog - Behaviour and Misbehaviour.

O'Farrell, V., (1994) - Dog's Best Friend.

O'Farrell, V. and Neville, P., (1994) - Manual of Feline Behaviour.

Olesen, I., (1976) - Old English Sheepdog.

Owren, T., (1982) - Communication with the Dog when Training.

Pavlov, I.P., (1927) - Conditioned Reflexes.

Peachey, E., (1992) - Runing Puppy Classes.

Peachey, E., (1993) - Good Puppy!

Pemberton, P.L., (1973) - Canine and Feline Behavior Control: Progestin Therapy.

Peirce, C.S., (1958) - Selected Writings.

Petersen, J., (1978) - Spaniels.
Ploog, D.W., (1966) - Biological Bases for Instinct and Behaviour: Studies on the Development of Social Behaviour in Squirrel Monkeys.'
Popper, K.R., (1962) - The Logic of Scientific Discovery.
Popper, K.R., (1972) - Objective Knowledge.
Pryor, K., (1975) - Lads Before The Wind - Diary Of A Dolphin Trainer.

Quine, W.v.O., (1961) - From a logical point of vue.

Rogerson, J., (1991) - Understanding Your Dog.
Rogerson, J., (1992) - Training Your Dog.
Rothausen, B., (1977) - Ulven Samson - en ulv blandt mennesker.
Ryan, T., (1994) - Alphabetizing Yourself—Help Your Dog Regard You as Leader.
Ryan, T., (1994) - Games People Play... To Train Their Dogs.

Schlick, M., (1949) - Philosophy of Nature.
Schneider, E., - Know Your Cocker Spaniel.
Schwizgebel, D., (1983) - Zusammenhänge zwischen dem Verhalten des Tierlehrers und dem Verhalten des Deutschen Schäferhundes im Hinblick auf tiergerechte Ausbildung.
Scott, J.P., Fuller, J.L., (1965) - Genetics and the Social Behaviour of the Dog.
Sebeok, T.A., (1977) - How Animals Communicate.
Seligman, E.P., (1975) - Helplessness.
Serpell, J.A., (1986) - In the Company of Animals.
Silvanus., (1995) - Med hundehilsen TOF.
Skinner, B.F., (1938) - The Behavior of Organisms.
Skinner, B.F., (1974) - About Behaviorism.
Smith, J.M., (1958) - The Theory of Evolution.
Storr, A., (1968) - Human Aggression.
Sundgren, P.E., (1975) - Bedre hundeavl.
Stöhr, H., (1976) - Hvordan hjælper man sin syge hund.
Sørensen, L., (1983) - Bogen om spidshunde.

Thorne, C., (1992) - The Waltham Book Of Dog And Cat Beahaviour.
Thomsen, P., (1983) - Pattedyr.
Tinbergen, N., (1953) - Social Behavior in Animals.
Toftesgaard, B., (1986) - Fra hvalp til voksen lydig hund.
Trumler, E., (1971) - Mit dem Hund auf Du.
Trumler, E., (1977) - 1000 tips til hundevenner.

Ullman, H.J & E., (1980) - Min spaniel.
Ursin, H., (1982) - Neurophysiology of Behavior.

Van Hooff, J.A.R.A.M., (1966) - The Facial Displays of Catarrhine Monkeys and Apes.

Van Larwick-Goodall, H.J., (1970) - Uskyldige Dræbere.

Van Larwick-Goodall, H.J., (1971) - In The Shadow of Man.

Verga, M., (1982) - Relative influence of Genetic and Environmental Factors on the Behaviour of German Shephard Dogs and Rottweilers.

Voith, V.L., (1982) - Possible Pharmacological Approaches to Treating Behavioral Problems in Animals.

Voith, V.L. & Borchelt, P.L., (1985) - Elimination Behaviour and Related Problems in Dogs.

Voith, V.L. & Borchelt, P.L., (1985) - Separation Anxiety in Dogs.

Voith, V.L. & Borchelt, P,L., (1985) - History Taking and Interwiewing.

Voith, V.L. & Borchelt, P.L., (1985) - Fears and Phobias in Companion Animals.

Vollsted, R., (1981) - Kontaktadfærd og motivation hos Vuples vulpes.

Watson, J.B., (1930) - Behaviorism.

Whitney, L.F., (1971) - How to Breed Dogs.

Wickler, W., (1967) - Socio-Sexual Signals and Their Intraspecific Imitation among Primates.

Wilkes, G., (1996) - Click & Treat—Training Kit Version 1.1.

Wood-Gush, D.G.M., (1983) - Elements of Ethology.

Woodhouse, B., (1986) - Dog Training My Way (1. udgave 1973).

Wright, R., (1994) - The Moral Animal.

Wyant, C., (1978) - Heelaway your Dog.

Wyant, C. Lewis, P., (1979) - Your Dog's training.

Zinkernagel, P., (1962) - Conditions for Description.

Zimen, E., (1981) - The Wolf - his Place in the Natural World.

Åmund, J., (1983) - Hund i byen.

Roger Abrantes, PhD in Evolutionary Biology and Ethology, born in Portugal, has lived in Portugal, UK, Denmark, Australia and Tanzania before he moved to Thailand in 2005.

He is the author to 19 books in English, German, Spanish, Italian, Portuguese, French, Danish, Swedish, Norwegian and Czech; and numerous articles and blogs.

He is probably one of the most versatile ethologists in the world. His work ranges from lecturing at the **Ethology Institute**, where he is the scientific director, to appearances as guest lecturer at universities world wide, popular talks and seminars, and advisory work for police departments. He was also the instructor of the trainers of the famous landmine and tuberculosis detecting rats.

He has written popular books with sound advice to pet owners as well as scientific papers. He teaches ethology, animal learning and epistemology. He is a popular guest in TV and radio programs having appeared in shows in many countries.

His English books *Dog Language–An Encyclopedia of Canine Behavior* and *The Evolution Of Canine Social Behavior* became hits the moment they reached the US bookshelves.

Dr. Abrantes is known for his views on social behavior and its applications to the understanding of pet behavior; and for his working method, *psychology rather than power*.

He is also a versatile animal trainer having worked with dogs, wolfs, foxes, cats, horses, rats, guinea pigs, seals and parrots.

His present work involves giving seminars and writing articles and blogs. He is an avid *seaman*, frequently sailing and diving in the South Andaman Sea, studying and enjoying the rich marine life of this region.

Facebook: https://www.facebook.com/abrantesroger
Tweeter: https://twitter.com/abrantesroger
Blogsite: http://rogerabrantes.wordpress.com
Website: https://www.abrantes.org

The Evolution Of Social Canine Behaviour

by Roger Abrantes

This book is a detailed study of the evolution of canine social behaviour. The author leads the reader, step by step, through the various aspects involved in the development of single social behaviour patterns. This book is also a comparative study, where the reader is lead from one argument to the next with mathematical precision.

A surprising book, dismissing common believes and assumptions, and leaving the reader with simple sound explanations. A book for all students of animal behaviour, as well as for all readers fascinated by animal behaviour wishing to uncover the whys and hows of canine social behaviour.

Dogs Home Alone

by Roger Abrantes

Home Alone is the canine behavior problem that we treat with greatest success. The program described in this book will help dog owners to teach their dogs to cope with being left alone. Readers can also advantageously use this book to prevent the problem from showing up.